Up, up and Away

Hello!

KENT

Edited by Lucy Jenkins

First published in Great Britain in 2000 by
YOUNG WRITERS
Remus House,
Coltsfoot Drive,
Woodston,
Peterborough, PE2 9JX
Telephone (01733) 890066

HB ISBN 0 75431 994 6
SB ISBN 0 75431 995 4

FOREWORD

This year, the Young Writers' Up, Up & Away competition proudly presents a showcase of the best poetic talent from over 70,000 up-and-coming writers nationwide.

Successful in continuing our aim of promoting writing and creativity in children, our regional anthologies give a vivid insight into the thoughts, emotions and experiences of today's younger generation, displaying their inventive writing in its originality.

The thought, effort, imagination and hard work put into each poem impressed us all and again the task of editing proved challenging due to the quality of entries received, but was nevertheless enjoyable. We hope you are as pleased as we are with the final selection and that you continue to enjoy *Up, Up & Away Kent* for many years to come.

CONTENTS

Edward Britton	42
Thomas Sparrow	42
Julie Gill	43
Katie Hutton	43
Adel Ready	‚44

Downe Primary School

Felicity Lever	44
Bruce Castle	45
Emma Dalziel	45
Emma Grant	46
Katie Beard	46
Dominique Wells	47
Daniel Gilbrook	48
Jessica Phillips	49
Aaron Farron	49

Hollingbourne Primary School

Josh Dunmill	49
James Milner	50
Liam Broster	50
James Ferragamo	50
Ross McLoone	51
Evroyd Benjamin	51
Danielle Fitzgibbon	51
Luke Graham	52
Max Aitken	52
Tristan James Canty	53
Holly McCarthy	53
Francesca Stump	54

Kings Farm Primary School

Stephanie Weir	54
David Rawlins	55
Billy Turner	55
Kirsty Rea	56
Steven Coleman	56
Emma Leach	57

Danielle Fill	78
Mark Carroll	79
Rebecca Payne	80
Kerry Hamill	81
Adam Fill	82
Katie Thurkle	82
Holly Rose Louise Heath	83
Nicola Codling	84
Govinda Singh Bhakar	85
Nadine Wheeler	86
Alice Childs	86
Kylie Newport-Dempster	87
Florence Edridge	88
Phoebe Troy	89
Debbie Charlton	89
Rosie Bannister	90

Pembury Primary School

Ian Matthews	90
Jonathan Anstey	91
Oliver Hall	91
Emma Julie Henson	92
Lauren Beeching	92
Callum David Rennie	93
Rory Gilbert	93
Jack Vaughan	94
Sarah Hendley	94
Joanna Curry	95
Craig Waters	95
Emma Newton	96
Katy Shelton	96
Laura Masters	97
Kevin Everest	97
Harvey Green	98
Clare Richards	98
Kelly Heath	99
Lucy Rudge	100
Lydia Burgess	100

Arthur Mazzey	101
Jessica Woodgate	101
Stephanie Dunn	102
Lauren Fitzgerald	102
Adam Merrin	103
Elizabeth Drapper	104
Ross Bromley	104
Matthew Rice-Tucker	105
Les Chaffe	105
Luke Hattle	106
Sarah Tollefson	106

Perry Hall Primary School

Emma Shiel	107
Hope Watson	107
Abbi MacAllister	108
Kristi Cormack	108

Poverest Primary School

Charmian Oakes	109
James Cresswell	110
Katie Norman	110
Christopher Miles	111
Ben Howard Shearn	111
Vanessa Thurgood	112
Sarah-Jayne Gibbs	112
Jack Fawcett	113
Rachel Darby	114
Cassey Gaywood	114
Jenny Bassett	115
Cathy Alcoran	115
Tara Short	116
Natasha Sweetlove	117
John Parker	117
Lisa Daynton	118
Chloe Mitchell	118
Louise Fox	119
Laura Fitzgerald	120

St Margaret's CE Primary School, Tonbridge

St Ronan's School, Hawkhurst

Joshua Pickup	198
Alex Macintyre	199
Hugo Kemball	200
Niall MacCrann	201
Anna Munro-Faure	201
Charles Beecroft	202
Marc Faure	202
Charlie Houghton	203
Edward Page	203
Hugo Brodie	204
Charles Weston Smith	205
Edward Grissell	205
Kiloran Campbell	206
Bertie Blundell	207
Alex Kelin	207
Michelle Faure	208
Harry Hoblyn	208
Jonathan Ross	209
Toby Walker	209
Marcus Hall	210
Edward Beecroft	210
Charlotte Peniston	211
Alastair Borland	211
Charles Harris	212
Ben Wilkinson	212
Theo Kingshott	212

St Teresa's Catholic Primary School, Ashford

Ciara Masterson	213
Jonathan William Fearne	214
Alexander O'Malley	214
Kandice Fernandes	215
Rachel Leavey	216
Nicola Perry	216
Grace Kettle	217
Amanda Jowett	218
Maggie O'Sullivan	218

Hannah Quinn	219
Matthew Burchett	220
Mathieu Walsh	220
Emma O'Brien	221
Morgan Davies	222
Maddison Leigh Coke	222
Elliot Hulland-Kemp	223
Michael Sparks	224
Danielle Sarah Ratcliffe	224
Jessica O'Reilly	225
James Aglony	226
Alex O'Connor	226
Rachael Bailey	227
Sarah Byrne	228

Shernold School

Freja Ludlow	229
Sophie Sandison	229
Mira Ambasna	230
Sarah Crouch	230
Abby Savage	231
Emma Ghosh	232
Alessandra Scala	232
Rosemin Anderson	233
Ellie Bliss Chirnside	233
Alexandra Allin	234
Laura Howell	234
Jade Jasmine Francis	235
Charlotte Lepora	235
Natalie Brockwell	236
Jane Costello	237
Amy Hartfield	237
Rachel Crane	238
Victoria Webb	238
Alice Bettney	239
Rebecca Harris	239
Victoria Edwardes	240
Jennifer Cosgrove	240

The Poems

RUBBISH

Rubbish dropped out of cars,
All along the road.
Giving off disgusting smells,
So everyone should know.

Rubbish floating on the sea,
Should be in the bin.
Disgusting smells drifting out,
Of each and every rubbish bin.

Rubbish strewn along the beach,
Made by you and me,
We should help all the world,
To stop this monstrosity.

Kate Boulden & Amy Laker (11)
Aldington Primary School

CHOCOLATE, CHOCOLATE

Chocolate, chocolate what a lovely thought
Melting in my mouth.
Light chocolate, dark chocolate
Has a crunching sound.
Chocolate on ice-cream
Chocolate on cake.
Triple chocolate cookies
Cookies and cream.
Mmmm chocolate, chocolate.

Morgan Richter & Holly Chambers (10)
Aldington Primary School

BOOKS AND BIKES

When I look,
In my motorbike book,
I begin to wonder,
If I could buy a Honda.
I begin to herd,
On a Honda Blackbird.
Soon I rave some,
About a Harley Davidson.
Then I pull a daring raid,
On my Honda Fireblade,
When I think I'm all lost,
I think about a Kawasaki Dirt Cross.
Then I gather some thoughts,
And pull together an Asprillia Sport.
Then my mates say 'I love you,'
When I'm riding my BMW.
Then suddenly my mind went blank,
I was only dreaming,
With the book on a hooter,
On a Peugeot scooter!

Denika Walsh & Stephen Smart (11)
Aldington Primary School

SQUIRREL

Squirrel leaping from branch to branch in the air,
He sees a forest full of acorn trees,
The most perfect view anywhere,
Squirrel scuttles through the golden leaves,
Squirrel searches acorns, conkers, nuts everywhere.

I see my little squirrel in his drey,
His bushy tail is so soft and grey,
I love watching my little squirrel, it is such a joy,
Oh, the pleasure of having a little friend nearby.

Lizzie Boulden & Lewys Jones
Aldington Primary School

AFRICAN PLAIN

As the hot, watery sun rises,
The animals begin to awake,
In the morning sun,
As the lioness gives a mighty roar

There is a stampede of gazelles,
The lions gaze at a baby gazelle,
The pride of lions ascend,
Then the great chase begins

The pride of lions pursue,
The infant loses its balance,
As helpless as a little worm,
The pride tuck into a marvellous feast

Then all is quiet and peaceful again,
Except for the vultures,
Who were tucking into the gruesome bones,
The lions are asleep,
The sun is setting behind the plain.

Lucy Bateman (10) & Eleanor Boulden (11)
Aldington Primary School

SCHOOL

Class boring,
Miss, he's snoring.

Playground loud,
Why is there a crowd?

School dinners, sick,
Get the bucket quick!

Playtime again,
Nine times ten.

Home time at last,
School is in the past.

Lauren Abraham (10)
Aldington Primary School

BOOKS

Thin books,
Fat books,
Long books,
Short books,
Bibles, poems,
Story books galore.

Horror books,
Love books,
Bad books,
Good books,
Bibles, poems,
I love *books.*

Emily Cackett (10)
Aldington Primary School

PONIES

Getting into the groovy mood,
Never bumpy, always smooth,
Trotting along in the countryside,
Letting the pony take your ride,

We're jumping up and falling down,
Always looking all around,
Cantering along the countryside,
Looking forward to scotch eggs fried,

I'm so happy and glad too,
That is why I'm sharing these secrets with you
Come along another day and shout a big . . .

Hooray!

Megan Knight & Jenny Green (10)
Aldington Primary School

SCHOOL

School has begun, kids all run.
Off to class, Jamie is always last.
Teacher snoring, work is boring.
Bells are ringing, teacher singing.
Teacher shouting, kids on outing.
Bells are ringing, break is beginning.
The choir singing kids rule teachers drool.
Class again, 10 times 10.
Maths is stinky, I'll play with slinky.
Lunch has started, Bill has farted.
Class once more, Jill has broken the door.
Home time at last, school was a *blast!*

Jenni Reeves (10)
Aldington Primary School

OVER THE FIELDS AND THROUGH THE WOODS

I love the smell of pony nuts of saddle soap and leather,
But the smell of horses is far, far better,
I walk into the tack room over to the saddle rack,
To collect the saddle and bridle,
My pony Misty's tack.
When I'm riding through the woods,
Trotting slowly on,
I feel that I could ride all day until the light has gone.
Riding back in the evening through the setting sun,
I know I've had a great time but now the day has gone.

I really love the feeling of a saddle on my back,
And the feeling of excitement when we're going on a hack.
As I trot through woods of green,
Dotted with woodland flowers,
I really feel I could go on for hours and hours and hours.
As I trot through lovely meadows,
Dotted with tiny daisies,
And the sun bears down upon my back,
I begin to feel quite lazy.
Trotting back in the evening through the setting sun,
I know I've had a great time but know the day has gone.

Rosie O'Driscoll
Aldington Primary School

RIDING MY PONY

I walked in the tack room,
And smelled the clean leather.
I looked through the window and saw the bad weather,
But that would not stop me from riding my pony,
I would ride him bareback,
Although he's quite bony.
I trot through the wood for as long as I could
Then I canter back down, until he's turned brown.
He stands by the stable and starts to get washed.
While over his back, the clean water gets sloshed.
Then the brown mud creeps slowly down and down,
Then suddenly drips right onto the ground.
After the ride, he gets washed and dried.
He gets put in the stable to show off his pride.
After the ride.

Rachel Muir (10)
Aldington Primary School

GALLOPING ACROSS THE BEACH

I go down to the beach on my elegant thoroughbred,
He starts to trot down the golden sand,
I nudge him on and he starts a long delicate canter.
Through the waves we go, the cold, salty sea water,
Splashing against my horse's legs.
Then he gathers up speed and starts a gallop,
The cold wind is blowing my hair and lapping against my face.
The day is nearly over, I watch the beautiful pink clouds and the huge
Orange sun setting, down, down into the calm blue sea.

Annabel Cross (11)
Aldington Primary School

SCHOOL

School dinners yucky,
And very, very mucky,
We sit around a table,
Eating mouldy mustard,
Mixed with loads of custard.

Back to class, Sam's always last,
Teacher's snoring, work is boring,
Home time at last, hip, hip, hip, hip hooray, *yeah!*

Louise Laker (9)
Aldington Primary School

MY MIND

My mind is like a maze with loads of doors
I go to and some I don't.
In my mind I think about the sky and colours that are
floating around and around.
In my mind it is blurry and very dizzy, dizzy and colourful.
Sometimes I have dreams that go straight away,
and nightmares that I can't get out of my mind.
In my mind I see traffic lights flashing on and off,
green, red and yellow.
In my mind it is like a holiday, and I'm on the biggest,
tallest, scariest roller-coaster in the world.
In my mind I dream of winning the lottery.
In my mind I think of living on the beach, and getting
nice and tanned and feeling the hot sand against
my feet as I walk.
I see the warm blue sea splashing against the rocks.
My mind is like a maze, some doors I go to and some doors
I don't and that will stay there for life.

Leanne McKinley (10)
Blenheim Junior School

THE GIFT OF MY MIND

The gift of my mind is like a palace busy and buzzing,
Rich gold, rich reds, rubies galore.
All I see is bright lights shining on me.
My mind is like a palace busy and buzzing.
I have a special secret room, you open the door.
And there is my own special beach.
I go down the stairs on a ruby-red crystal carpet chandeliers
glaring at me,
My mind is like a palace, busy and buzzing.
My secret garden is beautiful and big,
There are fantastic, fluorescent floodlights beaming down onto
the bluebells.
I keep on going, there is a door with a massive padlock.
Nobody goes in there apart from me,
It is dark, dismal and black,
I think of things that upset me and things that I don't want anybody
to know.
My mind is like a palace, busy and buzzing,
But not forgetting my best room of all,
The music room, its hip, hop and happening,
There's my disco ball, my lights and my brilliant bubbles
and with loud music.
My mind is like a palace, busy and buzzing.

Hannah Yates (11)
Blenheim Junior School

MY MIND IS A GIFT

In my mind I wonder what the world will become,
In my mind I have a palace,
It's full of twisting colours
Sparkles and balloons are floating out of fluorescent floodlights.
If you were to go there, you would have to wear sparkle glasses.
In my mind I can feel fizzing fireworks.
I have a special room, it's full of sparkles
You can smell sweets
There's pure gold chairs and, crystal clear chandeliers.
Ruby-red stairs with gold sparkles.
In my mind I see disco balls.
In my mind it's a festival of shooting stars,
I can hear sparkles bursting everywhere.
If I go into a different room,
It's got a sparkling swimming pool
With opal curtains all around it.
In my mind I can hear pianos tinkling
And violins playing in the distance.
In my mind I can see candles.
If I think really hard,
I can turn on the sparkle and fluorescent floodlights.

Rachael Hill (11)
Blenheim Junior School

FOOTBALL FEVER

The ball rolls along with pace and swerve.
The tackles were hard, we never held back
That's when we started to plan our attack.

The tactics were right, we played like a dream
That's how we played the boys in green.

3-0 was the final score and we wiped
The team into
The floor.

When we won the School Cup we felt like
We were in heaven -
Can you guess the team?
Yes! It was Blenheim.

David Arnold (11)
Blenheim Junior School

THE HORRIBLE SURPRISE

It was a miserable day, may I say
It was a rainy day
All ugly and grey.
I was walking along
Singing a song
Until I heard a bong, bong.
So I ran into school
All calm and cool
Until I saw a ball
Rolling down the hall
And I heard a call.
Then I got hit by the ball
And smacked right into the wall
Which was thick and tall
Cold and cool.
And I had a bad head
So I asked the Doctor and he said,
'You must go straight to bed
And rest your head.'
So I did what the doctor said.

Hayley Algeo (10)
Blenheim Junior School

THE GIFT OF MY MIND

Inside my mind
I can see the day just drift away,
Like a cloud floating in the sky.

In my mind I feel pain
Where all of my memories
Are stuck in here forever
Like a story engraved in stone.

In my mind I see my dreams
And they all come true for me
Like a tree
Trying to reach for the sky.

In my mind I can see
The blaze of fright and fear of the flashing lights
That dazzle me inside
Like a shooting, silvery star.

In my mind
I can see the places
Like a stranded island
Others are like a one-way road
And there is no turning back.

The real gift of my mind
Is the one door which has secrets inside
Secrets only I know
And nobody else will ever find out!

In my mind
I can see the day just drift away
Like a cloud floating in the sky.

Hayley Micallef (10)
Blenheim Junior School

IN MY MIND I SEE A GIFT

In my mind, in the night
Everything comes to life
With the centre of life
With a heart full of souls
Called the heart of life.
In my mind I see a palace
Full of luxury treasures
And food fit for a king.
With gin, boar and all the other sweet and succulent food
And a servant skimming through his cook book
And just outside, a paradise awaits for someone to explore
But a dream can't last forever
So next time you're asleep - explore your own paradise.

Jamie Venn (11)
Blenheim Junior School

THE WOODS

The moon shines on an icy cloud
Animals and insects cry aloud.
Spider's weaving, flies leaving
Down on a misty field . . .

By the luscious woods you see a
Rider with a hood. With a splash
She makes a dash from the place she
Stood. Alone at last, the woods are free
You must let life and beauty be. You
See the gleam of a frosty stream, Oh,
It's so like a dream.

Samuel Heard (9)
Blenheim Junior School

MY MIND

In my mind I am a clear blue sky,
looking down at everyone.
In my mind the sun is beside me
protecting me.
In my mind people look at me and say
'What a lovely sky!'
In my mind I think I will live forever.
In my mind I think blue is a clear and
everlasting colour.
In my mind I am very bright
and beautiful.
My mind will live forever.
In my mind I think about family,
secondary school, SATs tests, friends,
old pets and a lot more.
In my mind I watch everything people do.

Gemma Mann (11)
Blenheim Junior School

IN MY MIND IS A GIFT

Playtime it's playtime
Playtime means break time
Play football, play it, play skipping
Play cricket
Playtime it's playtime
We have lots of fun
Joy and excitement under the sun
Playtime it's playtime
Time to have snacks
'Look at this mess of crunchy crisp packs!'

Clare Wright (10)
Blenheim Junior School

GIFTS IN MY MIND

In my mind I'm on a roller-coaster
Hurtling up
And down,
Quickly going all the way
Up to Heaven,
Then going
Down to Earth and . . .
All the way down to the ground.

In my mind I'm a snail
Slowly sluggishly moving
On the warm green grass
Whilst looking at the sparkling dew.

In my mind I'm a rally driver
Coming up with ideas
To get past obstacles.
My perspiration running down my face,
My hands shaking like a goalkeeper.

In my mind I'm a king
Ordering people about.
Feeling proud of myself
Whilst sitting on my throne
And wearing my crown.

In my mind I'm a tiger,
Chasing a jackal
In the warm mists of the jungle
I can smell the fear of the jackal.

In my mind, nothing is impossible
But in reality you just have to wait and see!

Matthew Tellinghusen (10)
Blenheim Junior School

MY MIND HAS MANY GIFTS

In my mind I have silly thoughts
of dying in a battle fort.
In my mind I dream of getting
married in the year 1999 or 2000.
In my mind I think of my mum
turning into a dragon - my dad a women.
In my mind I have silly dreams of
the bad things that I've done.
In my mind I dream of becoming the
next David Beckham or Dwight Yorke.
In my mind I think of the world
being blown to smithereens.
In my mind I have silly thoughts
of the world being knocked down.
In my mind I have a dream
of becoming an astronaut.
In my mind I think of
the world living in peace
and in my mind I see the
world living as one.

Aaron Garrard (11)
Blenheim Junior School

WHERE'S THE TORTOISE NOW?

There's a tortoise in our bath
That always loves to laugh
I think it always laughs
Because it saw me in the bath

There's a tortoise in our loo
That loves to use shampoo
He loves to eat bamboo and
Has a tattoo on his soft shoe

There's a tortoise in our shower
That loves to play every hour
When I turn on the shower
He shouts out 'You have the power!'

There's a tortoise in our sink
That loves the colour pink
I don't know why but he loves to blink
And yesterday he started to stink.

Hanane Benyermak (11)
Blenheim Junior School

MY HEAD

My head is like shooting stars
My head is like a swimming pool
My head is like a bouncy castle.

My head is like a maze
My head is like a deep dark cellar
My head is like the moon.

My head is like the moonlight beams
My head is like flashing beams
My head is like the stars that twinkle in the sky.

My head is like a wiggerly fish
My head is like a dolphin
My head is like a shark.

My head is like a brake
My head is like a palace
But last, but not least
My head is all screwed up.

Sadie Drake (10)
Blenheim Junior School

MY MIND

In my mind I can see the bright lights
Blue dazzling lights making my eyes go blurry.
Then changing to red then green.
Mirrors all around me reflecting.
In my mind I am travelling place to place.
I am flying everywhere.
I can see red, blue, green, black and gold - all blurry.
Bright lights - dim lights - blurry lights.
Travelling everywhere fast
. All the sparkling fireworks around me in my mind.
Disco lights flashing in my eyes
In my mind I look at the sky and see bright twinkling stars.
Then in my mind I am going to a dark place
A dark dim place.
Through a dark tunnel that never seems to end.

Lisa Bignell (11)
Blenheim Junior School

THE BLUE LAGOON

There was once a blue lagoon,
That was surrounded by some baboons.
Then it was the end of June
So it was surrounded by some racoons.
Then there was a monsoon
And also the harvest moon.

There was once a blue lagoon
That was flooded by the monsoon
For some reason there was a spoon
And the spoon didn't move.
The baboons were scared of the racoons,
The baboons saw the spoon,
And used it as a shield from the racoons.

There isn't a blue lagoon,
That was flooded by the monsoon.
The baboons and racoons are now some cartoons
And now the blue lagoon is a water company.

Jake David Cashmore (10)
Blenheim Junior School

IN MY MIND I SEE A GIFT

In my mind I see a Charizard
As red as red can be
In my mind I see my mum and dad
Who love me very much.
In my mind I see my sisters
Playing merrily in the bedroom.
In my mind I see Tommy
Who I love very much,
In my mind I see Samantha
Who I love too much for words.
In my mind I see love for my family
Who help me when I need help?
In my mind I see Luke
Who loves a bash up.
In my mind I see Liam
Who loves to fight.
In my mind I see Digglet
Which evolves into Dugtria.
In my mind I see computers
That have loads of programs.

Jamie Cullern (11)
Blenheim Junior School

MY MIND IS A GIFT

In my mind I can see a complicated maze,
Soft and foamy, lime green and loads of levels.
When I bounce I go really high.

In my mind I have sad and happy feelings,
My maze is as hard as a rock when I am sad
And bouncy and light when I'm happy.

In my mind at school when I don't understand something,
I have a person just like me, my person stops at a dead end.
When I begin to understand,
My person knocks down the dead end
And I can carry on.

In my mind when I get an idea I go to a different level,
And every time it gets harder with a different route.

In my mind when I have a dream, months later,
My mind recalls it and my person goes back
To that part in the maze and does what the
Person did at that time.

In my mind I think what I think,
And believe what I believe and
Say what I believe.

So that is why my mind is mine.

Francesca Mercer (10)
Blenheim Junior School

A HOLIDAY

One day we went on holiday
Fifty whole pounds I had to pay.
I went to our summer home
And thought I'd rather go to the Dome.

The sand is as hot as the sun
So to the sea I had to run.
The sea is sky-blue
But it's dangerous too.

As I lay on the sand in the heat,
I felt like a piece of cooked meat.
My chest was bright red
And so was my head.

The next day on the beach I lay
With food and drink on a tray.
In the shade of the umbrella I stay,
Almost every single day.

After a week I'd had enough
Of all the holiday stuff.
So it was back to my friends,
Where this poem ends.

Nick Abousselam (10)
Blenheim Junior School

THE SNAIL

I know a very ugly snail
His shell is hard and lumpy
He's covered in slime from his head to his tail
And he is extremely grumpy.

He wanders round the back-garden
And when something blocks his path
He doesn't say ''scuse me!' or 'pardon'
And he doesn't know how to laugh.

He sits in his shell all day long
And moves when he gets a fright.
Well once he did something very wrong
One cold and misty night.

He slid along the lettuce patch
And onto a runner bean.
My grandpa came out (now here's the catch!)
He is very, very mean.

My grandpa came out in his big brown boots
And saw that ugly snail.
It once ate a flower, right down to its roots,
But now it started to quail.

He started to hurry across the grass
But my grandpa let out his hen.
She wouldn't let the poor snail pass
So she ate him there and then!

Tamara Michaud (11)
Blenheim Junior School

CLASS FIVE'S DAY

People whispering
'This is hard'
People copying each other
Daydreamer's dreaming
Grinning like a Cheshire cat.
'Are you listening?' says the teacher
'Yes, I am,' said the pupil.

Click, click - is people biting their nails
Slam, creak - is us opening and closing desks.
Fling - is us flicking pencils
Creak - goes the door
'Are you listening?'
'Yes I am.'

Noses being picked
'Shoosh! Be quiet!'
'This is a bit too hard'
'He's mad'
'What do you have to do?'
'Are you listening?'
'Yes I am.'

Ring, ring goes the bell for home time
Teacher asks us to go.
We take our bags off the pegs
And go
'Are you listening?'
Silence!

Victoria Alison Woolven (9)
Blenheim Junior School

BE QUIET

'Kerrie, I'm trying to get on with my work!'
Flicking pencils
People pulling faces
Daniel grinning like a cat
'Kerrie, I'm trying to get on with my work!'

Paul becoming invisible when work starts,
Danielle going red with embarrassment
Lee being naughty, not getting on with his work.
'Kerrie, I'm trying to get on with my work!'

Dropping pencils
Rubbing out
Biting nails
'Kerrie, I'm trying to get on with my work!'

Picking noses
Desks slamming
Stephanie being nagged
'Kerrie, I'm trying to get on with my work!'

Daydreamers
Singing
Chatting
'Kerrie, I'm trying to get on with my work!'
Ding-a-ling
Assembly.

Marie Jones (9)
Blenheim Junior School

HARRY BO'S FIRST DAY AT SCHOOL

In our class
Harry Bo's singing
Too much

In our class
Mrs Brown is shouting
Too much

In our class
Mrs Brown stinks the classroom
Out with coffee

In our class
Harry Bo's getting a
Valentine's Day card
From Ashley

In our class
Mrs Brown is talking to her
Invisible friend

In our class
David is off task because
Harry Bo's poking him.

Lee Dighton (10)
Blenheim Junior School

WORLD CUP 2006

England! England are the best
England! England are better than the rest.

Beckham running up the line
Owen scoring every time
Seaman saving all the goals
On penalties we rely on Scholes
So we can win in this town
And let Keegan jump up and down.

We love football - it's the best
Give us a chance to put it to the test
The World Cup belongs here
Everybody raise a cheer!

Wembley is the place to be seen
As the football is supreme.
The year 2006 is the time
So please FIFA give it a try.

Jessica Stroud (10)
Blenheim Junior School

MY MIND IS A GIFT

My mind is like a slow small sleeping sly dragon.
  My mind is like a fast fly flying about the Earth.
    My mind is like a little light lighting the room,
      My mind is like a sloping sliding star flashing.

Jamie M Bennett (11)
Blenheim Junior School

WHAT IT'S LIKE IN CLASS

Darntations!
I can smell coffee
I love you!
Coffee cups.
I wish we could do PE
Darntations!
I like school.
Can I carry on now?
Paint everywhere.
I wish we could go home.
Darntations!
Look at our new clock
Works really good.
Let's use your rubber
I can't do this.
The bell should go off
Darntations!
Whisper! Whisper! Giggle!
On task please!
You're doing well.
I like school
Darntations!
Yeah! We break up on Friday.
Tom have you got your ball?
This is what it's like in our class.

Daniel Poynter (10)
Blenheim Junior School

SMELLY COFFEE

On Friday David said
'Mr Watts are we doing PE?'
I smell coffee floating across my desk.
I heard the class talking and
Mr Watts class went into the music room.
Mr Watts said
'Are you listening?'
'Yes I am!'
Ding-a-ling
Assembly
Mrs Caffee said
'We will be planting a tree'
Home time
Ding-a-ling
Home.

Kieran David Watts (10)
Blenheim Junior School

NINE THINGS UNDER MY BED

A slimy snail in the corner of my bed
A shy spider that would not come out
A caterpillar that is possessive but kind
A huge elephant that can fit under my bed
A sock that smells like off Cheddar
A mouldy stuffed pizza
A sharp-clawed cat that ate dog food
A wild fox that comes at night
A shotgun that's really powerful.

Peter Finn (8)
Brook Community Primary School

THE PAST

In the Victorian Musical
entertainment room is -

A beautiful painting of a nude woman
a tuneful golden harp.
A triple branched glowing candle
a grand lacy dress fit for
a queen.
A pitch-black trunk full of goodies
with printed gold leaf patterns.

A piece of fine music artwork,
and the only sound
is a magical sound of
sorrowful singing.

Beth Jasmine King (9)
Brook Community Primary School

DEAR GRANDMA

I'm sorry for pouring spaghetti
all over your clothes and bouncing
on your belly and putting apple crumble
all over your telly.
I'm sorry for putting thorns on your lovely
comfy chair and scooping baked beans all
over your hair.
I'm sorry for putting dirt in your tea and getting
all of your private books out.
It must have been hard work clearing up after me,
and rushing about.

Hannah Marie Hopkins (7)
Brook Community Primary School

A BOX FULL OF DREAMS

Come ride with me in the box of dreams,
Where everything is not as it seems.
When I lie by the sparkling waters
The world is free from killings and slaughters.

The golden horses are colossal and free,
And the emerald green grasses grow up to the knee.
The sky is blue and the sun is yellow,
All the people are friendly and mellow.

These are only some of my dreams,
Else the dream box would be splitting at the seams.
The seeds of life are thriving again,
Sunshine or snow, wind or rain.

I feel as if my mind has blown,
With happy dreams no men have known.
The horrible dreams are kept at the back,
And they're only let out with a special knack.

I can't think how the dreams can form
Some come like thunder, raging in a storm.
Under the tree it is dreamy and cool
As all the animals drink at a crystal pool.

Ellie Pierce (10)
Brook Community Primary School

IN THE MUSICAL ENTERTAINMENT ROOM IS:

A beautiful painting of a young woman,
A tuneful golden harp playing a waltz
A burning candelabra
A huge fireplace with a pitch-black chimney
And a party fit for a queen

A dress as white as snow with jewels trickling down,
A cupboard filled with golden goblets
A floor with flowery patterns
An ancient ivory chair
And glorious tunes played by a beautiful harp.

Bethany Campbell (9)
Brook Community Primary School

DEAR SUZIE

I'm sorry about the magnificent beetles
in your fridge.
The bucket of slimy water carefully balanced
on your door.
I'm extremely sorry for eating your chickens
but they were mouth-watering.
The poisoned strawberry ice-cream was pretty dangerous.

And I'm dreadfully sorry, I don't know what
got into me
For pouring tea all over the nice clean carpet.
Sorry about the squashed worms in your bed
And definitely the goat's droppings
in your dad's pipe.

Is your hair still hurting from when I pulled it?
- not your brother!
I'm sorry about the coffee table and the magazines,
Sorry about the now well-known saying
'Suzie loves Harry Kitchen!'
With love from
you know who!

Camilla Hamer (7)
Brook Community Primary School

MY BOX OF NIGHTMARES

There I sit on the side of the road
I have been plagued by nightmares
I am waiting for a box to capture them.
The box is held up - so I am waiting.
Oh no! A nightmare is coming in to attack.
It takes ten seconds to strike. Ten seconds of terror.
(One) it's ready, (two) help, (three) I'm for it, (four) it's coming,
(five) I'll run, (six) I'm stuck, (seven) get me out of here!
(eight) it's coming, (nine) Oh no!
(ten) Aarrggghh! I'm done for.
It's got me! It's got me good and hard.
It's raining, it's starting, help it's evolving.
I should have known aahh!
It's started, I'm in a volcano - it's erupting.
I wake up, I scream, I come to my senses
It must have been a dream and I see . . .
My box of nightmares!

Louis Gauthier (10)
Brook Community Primary School

IN A SMALL FARMYARD

In a small farmyard is
A giant stone cottage beside a field
A muddy road leading to a huge pig-pen
Two tremendous pigs with dark black
Spots eating dry golden straw
A skinny women feeding them
Enormous cabbages with a
Bucket full of water
An old grouchy man racking the plants.

Jordan MacDonald (7)
Brook Community Primary School

A BOX OF MAGIC POTIONS

In my box of magic potions,
lurks a very extinct swirling mist.
A bellowing deadly cackle,
and a poisoned breath.
If you have a magic box of potions,
look inside it right at the back.
The bit laced with golden ribbon
and full of satin of the darkish red.
Look!
Can you see
a deadly thunder storm
and a bare tornado twirling
a lion's roar
and a packet of practical jokes?
Ha, ha, ha!
Do you have a magic box?

Emma Louise Keerie (9)
Brook Community Primary School

TEN THINGS IN MY CUPBOARD

A Pokémon toy of fiery dragon that roared.
A watch that tells the time around the world.
A costume that's big and hairy.
A Gobblemonster that gobbles gallons of rubbish.
A laptop that's battered and blind and a very fun kind.
A spider with eight or nine legs!
In the cupboard lies a dark shadow.
A marble that's pink and brown in a way.
A dark night's planets and stars in the universe.
A monster that is old and brown.

Alex Coleman (7)
Brook Community Primary School

TEN THINGS FOUND IN A WHALE'S STOMACH

A pile of wet slimy fish
A dead, sharp-toothed creepy, crawly black rat.
A beautiful mermaid that kept jumping about
The brave handsome Hercules trying to thump his way out.
The doctor, mad Lee, trying to figure a way to make
the whale even bigger.
A black cloud that keeps raining everywhere.
Ten children screaming because they're playing tag.
A giant sandwich that will gobble you up.
Sabrina The Teenage Witch casting spells everywhere.
A magic lamp with a magic genie that will grant
you three wishes.

Camilla Sutton (10)
Brook Community Primary School

TEN THINGS FOUND UNDER MY DESK

A tiny elephant
A person that can fly with wings,
Some pasta that never ends.
A huge tabby cat,
A giant green monster like 100 slimy worms.
A rabbit that eats anything,
A rubbery toy snake - all mouldy and old.
A teddy bear as big as a house.
A strange black Labrador eating cat food,
A shy Shetland pony.

Suzie Gilbert (7)
Brook Community Primary School

A BOX OF GHOSTS

A large box of slimy ghosts
They can make you shiver like a crazy cat.
Some are spooky just like you!
They are very grey - if you get close to one
You'll be scared out of your sparkling red shoes!
When they float under the door you are amazed.
The ghosts have gloomy eyes as big as a lion
And they're as frightening as a cheetah eating you
The strange thing is they have no legs and no arms
But they have old Victorian clothes!

James Tonkin (10)
Brook Community Primary School

TEN THINGS UNDER MY BED

Five dead slugs in a sock
A broken pair of glasses
Some hairs from a friend
A smelly old fish - out of water.
A toy car with no wheels
A baby looking for toys
A leaking bottle of blackcurrant squash.
A bag of money that belongs to Mum.

Daniel Keerie (7)
Brook Community Primary School

TEN THINGS FOUND IN A TEACHER'S POCKET

A broken pencil
A rusty fire iron
A metal whip
A set of yellow false teeth
A packet of headache tablets
A spoonful of nails help the headache go down
A card from the dumb Toni
A bucket full of children's hearts.
A vampire to fly her home
And a library full of gold!

Lee Ryan Brown (9)
Brook Community Primary School

APOLOGY TO A TEACHER

Dear Mrs Collingridge
Sorry for hitting you in the leg with an orange in science
Sorry for scribbling on your maths homework.
Sorry for my funny conversations in history.
Sorry for pulling funny faces in sharing assembly.
Sorry for putting water in the balloon in science
And popping it!
Sorry for putting worms in your cake at lunchtime.

Gemma Goodwin (8)
Brook Community Primary School

TEN THINGS FOUND IN A WIZARD'S TRUNK

Twenty gold Galleons
Emeric Switch's *Transfigurations made easy!*
An owl from his friend
A wand
An inherited useful invisible cloak.
Hogwart's homework timetable
A monster book of monsters.
Six eyeballs and ten teeth for potions.
A pile, the size of a mountain of homework
and a *much* needed relaxation spell.

Nick Baker (10)
Brook Community Primary School

BOX OF DREAMS

In my satin box of dreams
Where my dream is held.
At the back, tucked down the side
Is my golden horse waiting for me to ride.
Upon the misty meadow, galloping through the sky,
Together we will spread our wings and fly.
Now I have dreamed of that but, all I need to do,
Is unlock the dream box
To make my dream come true.

Emma Jean Tonkin (10)
Brook Community Primary School

BOX OF NIGHTMARES

In the box of nightmares
Where the ghosts just vanish,
Lightning strikes and thunder rumbles
Fire traps me. Can't get out!
Lost in the woods, where bears are
growling with hunger.
A horrible professor hides my dreams
Suddenly I wake up all hot and scared
Hear bumps on the wall *caboob!*
Be warned if you find the key
To this box, don't you
dare open it!

Cathy Hope Arnott (9)
Brook Community Primary School

A BOX OF WISHES AND DREAMS

In my box of wishes and dreams
My fairy holds my mystery fantasies.
My magic awaits upon my mind -
A little tree with flaming red mushrooms,
And tiny little holes where pixies have their meetings.
Mystery stars brighten my mind,
Wings that glow like the moon,
Glistening in the starry sky.

Iesha Bennett (9)
Brook Community Primary School

MY BOX OF MYSTERIES

In my box of mysteries
Where all the wondering lurks
There is something for everyone
Hidden deep inside its private space.
Maybe there will be ghosts, even UFOs
Or suspicious noises hidden in the darkness.
For others it maybe mysterious dreams
wondering what happened -
When suddenly you've awoken listening to a
distant cry.
But whatever lingers in your box of
mysteries
Remember I have mysteries too.

Lyanna Marie Reed (10)
Brook Community Primary School

A BOX OF DREAMS

In the box of dreams
Where things just float around
There are lots of funny flowers;
Animals that are weird, wonderful shapes,
Cats with no tails and only one eye.
A huge, giant palace that gloats upon soft clouds.
People that are always joyful.
It never rains,
There is no thunder or lightning.

Michael Wall (10)
Brook Community Primary School

A BOX OF DREAMS

In a huge box of dreams and nightmares
Where the winds howl loudly
A gigantic ghost keeps our dreams
Locked up in a tiny treasure chest
Full of dreams about Christmas
And nightmares about monsters eating people.
Then at night he scatters them onto you
So that you can't sleep.
If you do get to sleep he returns to haunt you.

Jeffrey Gilbert (10)
Brook Community Primary School

DEAR SIR KANGAROO

I am sorry for biting your leg
I thought it was a carrot,
I am sorry I called you a parrot.
I am sorry for eating all your food
I bet you're hungry now!
I think I'll go and get a cow!

Raymond Webb (10)
Brook Community Primary School

FUTURE

F uture is the year 2000
U nknown to all, we wait with anticipation
T omorrow may hold
U nexplained mysteries
R eminding us
E verything has a time.

George Colley (10)
Bybrook Junior School

DIVING, TWIRLING, DANCING

Diving, twirling, dancing,
Swimming deeper and deeper
In the clear garden pool.

Silvery-orange, sparkling,
Shimmering, shining -
Seeing companions
Playing at the pond edge.

Splashing through the fountain,
Enjoying hide-and-seek,
She feels excitement
Bubbling inside her.

Terrie Ireland (11)
Bybrook Junior School

THE INDIAN ENIGMA

I am an elephant.
I have duties
for a gorgeous lady wearing red
for today she will wed.
Her sari is scarlet,
the sun is saffron
glinting in her eyes.
When she arrives
she is greeted by her man in white.
Surrounded by golden corn, they wed.
I escort them to the Taj Mahal
where they pray
for love, happiness and peace.

Kelly Burns (11)
Bybrook Junior School

ALL HALLOWS EVE

A witch flies across the moon
L anterns flicker in the gloom
L ight comes from pumpkins bright

H allowe'en promises a night of fright
A ll spirits arise in the ebony black
L urching Grim Reaper carrying a sack
L ighting the way are jack-o'-lanterns in the dark
O ak tree carries the cross as the mark
W ebs glisten under the full moon
S wooping bat will find its dinner soon

E njoying the night, vampires suck blood
V ictim falls with a sickening thud
E very werewolf howls to the moon.

Edward Britton (10)
Bybrook Junior School

MILLENNIUM HISTORY

M i-lai massacre in Vietnam 1968,
I t's not the year 2000,
L iving differently from 1066,
L earning how Vikings lived in 800,
E ndless suffering through the wars,
N avaho - remember the Indian tribes?
N ew America, Columbus 1492
I n 2000 years the world has changed.
U nited Kingdom - born 1700s - all
M illennium history!

Thomas Sparrow (10)
Bybrook Junior School

MILLENNIUM CELEBRATIONS

M ystical colours, silver and purple,
I ncredible fireworks exploding, crackling.
L ate night laughter,
L ong queues for the Dome.
E vening celebrations that go on forever,
N ew views of London
N ightly from the Wheel
I n comes the new, out goes the old.
U nbelievable clothes and make-up worn at
M illions of parties around the world.

Julie Gill (10)
Bybrook Junior School

MILLENNIUM SCIENCE

M illenniums of magic magnets,
I nteractive computer games,
L ook at all the experiments,
L earning the meaning of science.
E lectronic failure - *Bug!*
N ational, international Internet.
N uclear bombs and neutrons smashed.
I ntroducing new inventions,
U nder sea technology and
M arvellous millennium medicines.

Katie Hutton (11)
Bybrook Junior School

MILLENNIUM FUTURE

M usic, madness and mayhem,
I ntergalactic space journeys -
L ights in outer space.
L ife and new species,
E nigmas of future years!
N ever-ending worlds,
 N ewborn untried planets,
I nvaded by UFOs - slavery!
U nderground towns and cities appear,
M oon holidays are here.

Adel Ready (10)
Bybrook Junior School

A LITTLE OLD LADY

A little old lady all lonely and poor,
Waiting and hoping for a knock at the door.

A little old lady all weary and sore,
Listening and praying for a knock at the door.

A little old lady can't take any more,
Frustrated and freezing, trying to open the door.

A strong wind breaks through, the door's open wide,
Then in comes an angel, the little lady has died.

Her spirit flies up to a beautiful cloud,
She's happy at last, not lonely, just proud.

Felicity Lever (11)
Downe Primary School

A WINTER'S TALE

Woolly winters every year,
Snowing softly, crystal clear.
Sweetening the chilled frosty air,
Excited children stop and stare.

The breeze swings silently through the trees,
Cold, freezing, shivering . . . can't help but sneeze!
The gripping, growling, ghostly gale,
Signals the end of another winter's tale.

Bruce Castle (9)
Downe Primary School

WINTER DAYS

Feel the shiver of your feet,
As you walk the icy street.
Feel it start with a growing gale,
Followed by the bitter hail.
Up above the leafless tree,
Fall the snowflakes filigree.
The snow lies lifeless on the ground,
Motionless, still, without a sound.
The snowmen will one day melt away,
But for now they're here to stay.

Emma Dalziel (10)
Downe Primary School

MY WINTER LAWN

The dawn is breaking,
The robins are waking,
The snow is all around.

The squirrels are scampering,
The snow is dampening,
The morning makes no sound.

The snow is falling,
The birds are calling,
Shattering the silence of dawn.

A fox wanders by,
All furry and sly,
The world of my winter lawn.

Emma Grant (9)
Downe Primary School

THE SNOW SNAKE

The snow falls,
It slides and crawls,
Its fangs are icicles, pointed and sharp,
Threatening menacingly in the dark,
Its camouflage hides away,
The dawning of a brand new day,
Its tongue is pointed like a rake,
The dangerously, slow, slippery shape,
A silhouette of the silent snow snake.

Katie Beard (10)
Downe Primary School

I Had A Dream

In my mind I saw the mist,
I crunched the white flakes in my fist.
A gust of wind, o, to and fro,
Winter is coming, autumn to go.
    Waiting,
    Waiting,
Waiting for the frosty snow.

Up in the sky the brightest star,
A distant hope, a wish from afar.
The ice was a diamond through the light,
All I could see was winter in sight.
    Icy,
    Icy,
Icy as I awakened the night.

A sudden sight of mistletoe,
Took me back to long ago.
A dainty snowflake, could it be,
Prints in silver filigree.
    Silent,
    Silent,
Silent as I turned the key.

Then I sat on a hard, grey stone,
And woke with a startle, a laugh and a groan.
It's just that I have been asleep,
And hoped that I could hold my weep.
    Dreaming,
    Dreaming,
Dreaming of winter next time to keep.

Dominique Wells (10)
Downe Primary School

THE LAUGHING SNOWMAN

I made a snowman in a field,
But now it's gone,
It must have been killed!

Then the next day to my surprise,
I saw my snowman,
Increased in size.

It must have been at least ten feet tall,
Fat and round,
Like a big snowball.

On its head was a hat and a scarf,
A carrot for a nose,
And it gave out a laugh.

I said to my snowman,
'Would you like to come and meet my clan?'
'Of course,' the snowman quickly replied,
'It's cold out here, it'll be warm inside.'

I went to fetch my family,
To show them,
Who was friends with me.

But when I returned, my clan in tow,
The field was empty,
The snowman had decided to go!

Daniel Gilbrook (10)
Downe Primary School

WINTER WONDERLAND

The filigree snowflakes are perpetually settling,
As fragile, fluffy snowballs fall,
The frozen lake is a mirror,
Reflecting the beauty of the season,
Crystallised icicles hang like ivory,
The silhouetted splendour of the scene is dazzling,
As the twilight gloom slowly approaches,
Signalling the end of another winter's day.

Jessica Phillips (10)
Downe Primary School

WINTER PLAYTIME

Over the bleak, barren snow,
Sledging, screaming as we go.
Scattering snowflakes all around,
They fall and land without a sound.
The children play without a care,
Passers-by stop and stare.

Aaron Farron (10)
Downe Primary School

THE STORM

The rain pours very quickly down upon the earth
And the thunder roars so loud it deafens.
The lightning flashes like a spotlight in the sky
And the clouds are so thick and black.
The wind is whirling round and round.

Josh Dunmill (9)
Hollingbourne Primary School

LEARN TO PLAY RUGBY

Always do the scrum, we never
Mind the weather, dull, bright,
Frosty, off to play we go
Win matches, lose matches
We never mind if we lose
Winning is not everything,
Well, not every time . . .

James Milner (8)
Hollingbourne Primary School

SHOOTING RAINBOWS

Bright red, bright yellow
Brightly shining
Like the sun
Glimpsing there
Here and there
Shooting rainbows everywhere.

Liam Broster (8)
Hollingbourne Primary School

THE DARK

I don't like the dark when I'm on my own,
I don't like it when I tiptoe upstairs,
When I got upstairs I saw something move,
It was only Mum and Dad coming back from Spain.

James Ferragamo (8)
Hollingbourne Primary School

SPACE

Out in space, far, far away are millions of stars and planets.
There is Pluto, Jupiter, Mars, Venus, Mercury and Earth.
If you went to outer space you would be floating in mid-air!
Sometimes in space an eclipse will erupt.
An eclipse is when the sun is behind the Moon.
Bye, bye, see you next year!

Ross McLoone (8)
Hollingbourne Primary School

THE SUN

The sun is hot, the sun is bright
The sun is shining in the sky,
It is so hot and it is so bright
It is so bright that it hurts my eyes
In the sky, very, very high.

Evroyd Benjamin (9)
Hollingbourne Primary School

KITES

Kites fly high up in the air
They are colourful, red, green, pink and all sorts of colours,
They fly on strings high up, I love to fly one
I love kites, I wish I could fly one every day.

Danielle Fitzgibbon (8)
Hollingbourne Primary School

SNOW

Crumbling, crunchy, mists of snow
Comes softly down one by one,
Up or down, left or right
There is always some in sight
In the garden, nice and peaceful
But up in the mountains, cloudy and noisy,
Wild, white winds fiercely sweep
Covering the ground with snow that's deep.
Skiers love to ride the snow
Down the mountains, watch them go!
Now the sun has come out to play
So the snow slowly melts away.

Luke Graham (8)
Hollingbourne Primary School

SPACE

Out there in the sky
There are millions of stars,
There are eclipses,
A rocket zooms into space,
The biggest planet, Jupiter
Made of gas,
Milky Way, full of dust,
Mars, made of lava,
Pluto, very hot,
The Earth is where I live,
It's huge!

Max Aitken (8)
Hollingbourne Primary School

FLYING HIGH IN THE SKY

Turning the propeller on,
Rolling on the runway,
We're going up, going up and we're off;
Birds are flying towards us,
Hope they don't hit us,
Going low a little,
Getting away from the birds
And now we are flying high in the sky!
We have got another mile to go,
Slowly going down,
Scratch go the wheels
We've made it,
We have had a good time flying high in the sky.

Tristan James Canty (9)
Hollingbourne Primary School

MY FIRST HOLIDAY

My first holiday was in Blackpool
I bought a ball
We ran into a big hall
We found some guides
I went on some rides
My best ride was a whizzing egg cup
I saw a big, big rubber duck
When I came out I was white
Was it the light?

Holly McCarthy (9)
Hollingbourne Primary School

THE HAUNTED HOUSE

Oh! There's a spooky cry
In the haunted house of *doom*
The ghosts are back to spook *again*
The weather is horrendous.
With *thunder crashing* and thumping down
And lightning that could *blind you*.
The hailstones come down, like a shark spotting its prey.
12.00 it's *Hallowe'en!*

Francesca Stump (9)
Hollingbourne Primary School

WHAT IS YELLOW?

What is yellow? Of course, the sun is.
The sun shines on us.
What is blue? The sky is blue.
It moves above the Earth.
What is green? A crocodile.
It goes *snap, snap, snap.*
What is grey? A rabbit is grey
That hops and hops.
What is orange? A railway man's suit
That a worker wears.
What is brown? A hamster is brown
That a cat eats.
What is peach? Our face is peach
That whirls in and out.

Stephanie Weir (6)
Kings Farm Primary School

WHAT IS GREY?

What is grey? A rabbit is grey
Hopping all around.
What is yellow? A pepper is yellow
In the shops.
What is blue? The sky is blue
When the sun comes out.
What is black? The sky is black
When the clouds are crashing everywhere.
What is red? Tomatoes are red
With my salad.
What is purple? Handwriting books
Are purple when we write in them.
What is white? The snow is white
When we go out playing.
What is pink? Our face is pink
When we run around.
What is green? The grapes are green
That we eat.

David Rawlins (6)
Kings Farm Primary School

MY DOG

Her teeth are blunt
She is funny
She rubs her face on the carpet.
She bites me.
My dog cries.
She is black and brown and white.

Billy Turner (6)
Kings Farm Primary School

WHAT IS WHITE?

What is white? Clouds are white
Moving in the sky.
What is grey? A rabbit is grey
Digging a home.
What is yellow? A yolk is yellow
In my egg.
What is green? A crocodile is green
Looking for food.
What is brown? A hamster is brown
Taking a nap.

Kirsty Rea (7)
Kings Farm Primary School

THE PLAYGROUND

Eat my crisps.
Play 'kiss chase'.
Play schools with Emma Leach and Kirsty.
Looking for tokens.
Playing 'stuck in the mud'.
Mario cars.
Kick the football.
Stephanie tickles me.

Steven Coleman (6)
Kings Farm Primary School

PATCH

Egg-shaped body
Twitches her nose.
A bit nervous.
Triangular ears.
Silky white.
Gobbles food.
Smooth skin.
Sharp teeth that bite.
She nibbles.
As brown as a nut.
Round, black eyes.

Emma Leach (6)
Kings Farm Primary School

CHIPS

As white as snow
Black as a blackboard
Claws as sharp as a razor
Eyes, round like a circle
A short tail
Smooth like a bird
Soft like an armchair.

William Pennell (6)
Kings Farm Primary School

PATCH

She nibbles food.
Her eyes are as black as a killer whale.
Patch is healthy
And as white as a cloud.
Patch has sharp nails
And fur as brown as a box
A little tail.

Jack Bennett (6)
Kings Farm Primary School

MY ADVENTURE

I'm swooping in the air,
I'm drifting in the clouds,
The birds are flying high
High up in the sky.

It's paradise up here,
Seeing the world's sphere,
I can hear the buzzing bees,
Flying in the gentle breeze.

It is so much fun,
Flying near the sun,
I have got an excellent view,
Of the world drifting by.

I can feel a very soft breeze,
In my paradise land,
Because I am going very fast,
In my aeroplane.

Lauren-Mae Chandler (9)
Mersham Primary School

DEAD BODIES

On Earth
We have just discovered
That
There is a
New planet
And this planet
Is so dangerous
That it is going
To
Invade
Earth
So our
Job is to
Save the
World. This
Planet is called
Pzzeyxxezad
And the
Bugs are
Eating
Dead
Bodies.

Ashley Bond (9)
Mersham Primary School

I LOVE HANGING TED ON MY KITE!

I love hanging Ted on my kite,
I've got to be careful or he'll bite.
He flies really high,
Right up in the sky,
I love hanging Ted on my kite.

He sees lots of birds,
And smells the fresh air,
But the problem is,
It's as simple as this . . .
I've lost my poor Teddy!

Sarah Webb (9)
Mersham Primary School

OFF IN SPACE

I'm out in space
Seeing the marvellous world
Then I get to planet Mars
I see super-duper aliens
'Oh no'
They're chasing me
I drive along the planet
I turn round
There's more
I will have to use my flying rocket.

Samuel Pendry (9)
Mersham Primary School

GUP, GUP AND AWAY

Flying frogs whooping,
Whirling in the air,
Cheeping chicks chiming,
Changing in their nests,
UFOs with urgaline urgary aliens,
Planes, polly, panting, palling in the sky,
The beaming sun,
Burning hot,
Like a chicken noodle pot,
Asteroid rocky, ranting, ruling space,
Hot air balloons hauling, hailing, hating clouds.

Hywel Williams (9)
Mersham Primary School

UP, UP, AWAY

The door opens
And I jump
Floating in the sky
Going down slowly
Very high
Shouting!
Now I am on
The ground and
I went

Splat!

Tania Ashman (9)
Mersham Primary School

UP IN THE SKY

Up, up and away,
I'm flying very high,
Up above the treetops,
High above the sky,
Near the fluffy, white clouds,
Birds flying all around,
I hear some hungry cheeping,
Sometimes angry squawking,
But mostly happy tweeting,
Now I'm getting lower and lower,
And now I've landed,
I've had a wonderful time!

Georgina Jephcote (8)
Mersham Primary School

ABOVE THE CHERRY TREES

Above the branches of the cherry trees,
Through the clouds and all the breeze,
A swallow is soaring very high,
Through the puffy clouds and up again,
Down on the ground it looks like Toy Town,
Cars like ants go crawling along,
May bells tinkling, daffodils, yellow,
All of them look so tiny and small,
Down again to make my nest,
Oh doesn't it look glamorous?
Oh doesn't it look good?

Bethan Forbes (8)
Mersham Primary School

PLANES AND HELICOPTERS

Planes flying through the sky
Like a smooth bird
Swishing through the light blue sky
But helicopters
Hitting planets and aliens
And all of the galaxies as well
And space rockets
Even flying saucers.

Justin Crux (9)
Mersham Primary School

OFF A PLANE

The door opened
and I jumped
I closed my eyes and I'm cold
It is high up
It is getting low
And *bang* - what a landing
I am wobbly and it
feels weird.

Charlie-Marie (8)
Mersham Primary School

INTO THE UNIVERSE

Going to space
A totally different place
Then see a funny face
Land on a planet.
Then unpack my suitcase
But now I'm going to see a space race.

I move onto Mars
To go and see the stars
But I don't know about the electric cars
Could go and see the stars
So I'll go drive the electric cars.

Now I move onto Jupiter
Where it looks even stupider.
Then I saw a skiddy spider
But then I saw a live screwdriver.

Benn Phillips (10)
Mersham Primary School

SOME PARROTS WHO COULDN'T FLY

Once in a land far away
Some parrots lived who couldn't fly
Why! Oh why!
They tried and tried
And then they cried
Why can't we fly?
Oh why! Oh why!

Lesley Andrews (8)
Mersham Primary School

THE SWEET I SAW IN THE STREET

In the street I saw a sweet
And it was so sweet
I ate the sweet
It tasted like meat
I got fatter and fatter
Until I was a ball
And then I went
Up, up and away
I went.

David Andrews (8)
Mersham Primary School

MARTIANS ARE IN THE SKY

Martians are in the sky
But I'm getting ready to fly
The Martians are coming down
But I think they are a bunch of clowns.
They have lasers but I only have a lousy sun razor.

Michael Laity (9)
Mersham Primary School

MAN FROM THE PLAINS

There once was a man from the plains
Whose job was to fly aeroplanes
He once flew too high
Fell out of the sky
And that's how he treats aeroplanes.

Jamie Temple (9)
Mersham Primary School

Up High In The Sky

5, 4, 3, 2, 1, 0, *blast-off*
We're flying up in the sky,
Up nice and high,
We're in a flying saucer,
Just you and I.

Above the trees,
And over seas,
High up in the sky we are.
I heard a jet,
Up in the sky,
That was flying nice and high.

I will fly to Mars,
Comets and stars,
I'm going up higher and higher.

It's starting to rain,
So I have to say 'Bye,'
But I will see you again,
Before I die.

Katie (9)
Mersham Primary School

Space

S   paceships fly high in the sky.
P   eople *shout* 'Hip, hip, hooray'
A   nd we all watch it on TV.
'C   an they make it?' people say.
E   mma shouts 'That is cool!'

Sophie Biggar (9)
Mersham Primary School

SCHOOL'S OUT

School's out, playing's in
Everyone shouts hooray,
School's out, playing's in
Let's all go and play.

School's out, playing's in
Joke books and quizzes are out
School's out, playing's in
So let's go to bed late.

School's out, playing's in
Get all of our toys out
School's out, playing's in
Let's run, scream and shout.

Everybody shouts *hooray!*

Lauren Williams (10)
Napier County Primary School

RAIN

I trickle down a window
I shimmer in the road.
I leave a silver trail
I sparkle in the night.
Sometimes I am a pretty sight.
I glimmer in the moonlight
I glisten on the path.
I shiver in the cold
I am just rain to the rich
And a drink for the poor!

Stacie Robertson (10)
Napier County Primary School

A SAD LONELY GOLDFISH

A sad lonely goldfish
No friends to play with
The poor old thing!

So sad and lonely
'Oh, please help me!'
I hear it cry.
Poor old thing!

Oh! So loud he whimpers
I wish I could help him.
Maybe I can
Poor old thing!

I know how I can
I can talk to him
And feed him
And play with him
Poor old thing!

So I will
Every day I will go down
I will, I will
Honestly.
He must be happy now
Poor old thing!

Katie Scott (10)
Napier County Primary School

DON'T !

Don't push your little brother off a boat
or ruin your mum's best coat.
Don't tear pages out of Dad's favourite book,
or run in the kitchen while Mum's trying to cook.
Don't be rude at the table,
or play around with the cable.
Don't feed the dog plates full of fish,
or take mice off your cat's dish.
Don't stick your fingers in the fish tank,
or rob the most famous bank.
Don't bend your ruler till it snaps,
or make the loudest claps.
Don't mess about with matches,
or put your fingers in catches.
Don't ever play on the tracks,
or hide in haystacks.
Don't run down the stairs,
or rock in the dining chairs.
Don't go under a train,
or get lifted up by a crane.
Don't put too much salt on your chips,
or burn your bright red lips.
Never-ever put ants in your pants.

Amy Mundell (8)
Napier County Primary School

FUNNY, FUNNY, FUNNY

Isn't it funny
That Pooh likes honey,
As honey is yummy
For Winnie the Pooh.

Isn't it funny
That Tigger hates honey,
As that is more honey
For Winnie the Pooh.

Isn't it funny
That Piglet eats honey,
As Piglet shares honey
With Winnie the Pooh.

Isn't it funny
That Rabbit buys honey,
As he hates honey
So he'll give it away to Winnie the Pooh.

Isn't it funny
That Owl hates honey,
He doesn't buy honey
For Winnie the Pooh.

Lisa Govans (11)
Napier County Primary School

MILLENNIUM

The millennium is a fun celebration for everyone to enjoy.

Music and dancing, the sound of Big Ben,
Cheering and singing.
Partying all night.
Champagne and silly string going everywhere,
Party poppers and whistles.
The loud sound of fireworks crackling in the sky,
Exploding and banging turning night into day.
They lit up the beacons to light up the world.
The River of Fire was such a sight
With all the colours and light.
A night I'll remember all of my life.

Ayesha Milner (8)
Napier County Primary School

LOVE SPARKLES

Love sparkles like diamonds
It sparkles like emeralds
Love - it sparkles like stars in the sky
Love - it sparkles like a sapphire
Or a beautiful ruby ring
Love - it sparkles like sunlight
On a stream or a lake
Love sparkles in the eyes of the person you love.

Emma Galloway (10)
Napier County Primary School

THE FLYING KITE

Flying a kite, flying a kite
How high can it go?
Fifty metres that's how high it goes.
What colour is your kite?
What colour is your kite?
Light blue, the colour of the sky,
Yellow, the colour of the bright sun,
Light green, the colour of the grass,
Red the colour of bright roses.
What's on your kite?
What's on your kite?
A little white rabbit with green eyes
Three flowers all standing up straight.

Rachel Carwardine (8)
Napier County Primary School

IS IT A SPACESHIP?

Is that a spaceship
Shiny and bright?
Up in the sky and up so high,
It looks like it's shy.
Because it's up to high
And never comes down.
Or can I be mistaken for the moon,
Shining so bright
Every night
In the lovely bright sky.
Where stars twinkle so bright
In the dark and gloomy night.

Chrysta Mellors (9)
Napier County Primary School

What's Going On?

By the blackboard
Children dropping chalk
Then treading on it.

By the cupboard
Kids ruining
Teacher's plans.

In the toilets
Girls
Doing their hair and make-up.

By the window
Boys pulling faces
At people as they walk past.

By the walls
Kids
Pulling off displays.

On the tables
Girls
Do the cat-walk.

On top of the cupboard
Children asleep
Snoring.

By the chairs
Kids
Cutting each other's hair.

In the playground
Dripping rain.
It's wet play!

Kylie McCafferty (11)
Napier County Primary School

MY FAVOURITE TIME OF YEAR

Spring:

Spring is coming, winter's going
New life everywhere.
Trees are budding, flowers growing
New life everywhere
Baby animals, baby birds
My favourite time of year.

Summer:

Summer's here, the sun is shining.
Holiday season's here
Everybody is going to the sea
Sun and sand - holiday season's here
Everyone is happy and excited
My favourite time of year.

Autumn:

Autumn's here - everything changes
Wind and rain is here
Leaves are falling, flowers dying,
Wind and rain is here
Birds flying away, animals hibernate
Some animals stay
My favourite time of year.

Winter:

Winter's here, everything is white
Now it's cold everywhere
Children playing, building snowmen
Now it's cold everywhere
Christmas is here now and another New Year
This is my favourite time of year.

Kayleigh Mills (8)
Napier County Primary School

THE RUNAWAY CAT

I have a cat
a black and white cat
but he has run away
because he is a runaway cat.

I haven't seen him since last year
his miaow, I would hear,
but he never comes home anymore,
because he is a runaway cat.

The runaway cat has black and white fur
with a thumb print on his chin,
he is a very sneaky cat,
because he is a runaway cat.

My runaway cat would chase flies all day
and make frogs scream, but just in play!
I see him do this no more
because he is a runaway cat.

Carla Lehane (11)
Napier County Primary School

FLOWERS

Flowers are red
Flowers are blue
Flowers are dead
Flowers are new

Flowers are sweet and so are you
Flowers are blue
Flowers are red
Flowers are new and so are you.

Flowers are nice to have next to your bed
Flowers have a sweetness like me and you
There are roses and daffodils all around the world.

Flowers are red
Flowers are blue
They have a sweetness and so do you.

Amanda Shipley (10)
Napier County Primary School

COLOURS OF THE RAINBOW

Red roses gleaming in the spring
Yellow sun shining happily in the summer
Pink flowers growing high in the sunny gardens
Green grass growing in the park
Green leaves growing on the trees
Orange drinks in the hot steamy summer sun
Purple violets scenting the air
Blue birds singing merrily in the treetops
These things remind me of a hot summer's day
When a rainbow is spotted in the deep blue sky.

Michelle Selby (10)
Napier County Primary School

The Moon Is Like

The moon is like
a round mirror
from heaven
that reflects light.

The moon is like
a white banana
that stands alone
away from the giants.

The moon is like
a round button
floating in the sky
keeping it together.

The moon is like
a drawn circle
coloured in white
put on black paper.

The moon is like
a white orange
that cannot be peeled
nor eaten.

The moon is like
a round cloud
that follows you about
everywhere you go.

Amy Stimpson (10)
Napier County Primary School

THE HANDS OF A CLOCK

The hands of a clock,
Sing tick-tock, tick-tock
They move continually all day long,
And all through the night they still sing their song,
Tick-tock, tick-tock.

The second hand does race,
Around the circular face,
Lap after lap it rotates,
Turning at its own special rate
Tick-tock, tick-tock.

Sixty stops around the clock,
Until it gets back to the top.
This hand keeps a steady pace,
Perfect timing less haste,
Tick-tock, tick-tock.

Twelve hours we sleep and twelve hours we wake,
A day - this long time does make.
Three sixty degrees twice around
The hour hand travels with its own slight sound,
Tick-tock, tick-tock.

Danielle Fill (11)
Napier County Primary School

LOVEY-DOVEY

When Mum and Dad go all lovey-dovey
we just don't know where to look;
My sister says 'Cut it out you two!'
While I stick my nose in a book.

Mum has this faraway look on her face,
while Dad has a silly grin.
'You don't have to mind us, kids,' he says,
We just wish they'd pack it in!

Dad calls Mum 'Little sugar-plum,'
and Mum says 'You handsome brute.'
Dad laughs and says, 'Look at Mum,
don't you think she's cute? I guess that's why
I married her, she's my truly wonderful one.'

Mum says he doesn't mean any of it,
but she thinks he's a lot of fun.
I just can't stand all the kissing!
At their age, they ought to know better;
I think I'll go up to my room
and write Jim'll Fix It a letter.

I hate it when they're lovey-dovey,
but I hate it more when they fight.
When faces redden and tempers flare
and sharp words cut through the night.

I'd rather they kissed and cuddled
and joked about and laughed.
At least we can tell everything's okay
when Mum and Dad are being daft!

Mark Carroll (10)
Napier County Primary School

SWIMMING IN THE POEM

Swimming in the morning
Swimming late at night
Swimming with a ghost
Will give you a fright

Swimming in the morning
Swimming before tea
Swimming in a swimming pool
Swimming in the sea

Swimming in the morning
Swimming late at night
Swimming in a shark pool
You're sure to get a bite

Swimming in the morning
Water up your nose
In your eyes
In your ears
And running through your toes

Swimming in the morning
Swimming on my back
Splashing in the water
With my friend Jack

Swimming in the morning
Diving through the air
Low board
Middle board
Highest if you dare

Swimming in the morning
With my family
Everybody's swimming
Swimming happily.

Rebecca Payne (8)
Napier County Primary School

GOD MADE US

God made light
God made dark
God made people
And God made us!

God made day
God made night
God made the sun
And God made us!

God made sand
God made water
God made Earth
And God made us!

God made you
And God made me
God made the world
And God made us!

Kerry Hamill (9)
Napier County Primary School

FOOTBALL IS FUN!

F ootball is fun
O ffside
O nside
T eaching to play
B ecause we need it
A ll the time
L oving football
L oving sport

I nside the
S tadium we play

F ootball is fun to play
U se of a ball
N ot in swimming

Adam Fill (9)
Napier County Primary School

THE OWL'S POEM OF PREY

The owl's eyes float elegantly,
Across the crystal skies.
But soon he needs to realise,
That his prey will soon pass by.

The owl sits in the old oak tree,
Waiting for his prey to come.
A full moon shines in the midnight sky,
While he watches his prey go by.

At last he sees a bewildered mouse,
Lying on the ground.
So the owl swoops for victory,
To eat the mouse alive.

Dawn breaks and the owl is sleeping,
Dreaming of the world going by
Until his feast of mice and rats will be,
His again
So until night he lies dormant,
In his old oak tree.

Katie Thurkle (10)
Napier County Primary School

LOOK

Look at the snow falling wide,
Look at the rivers, and the ebbing tide.
Look at the waves in the sea
Look at the fairies, it's a fantasy.
Look at the stars in the midnight sky,
Look at the clouds rushing by.
Look at the lilies in the stream,
Look at the moon and its starry gleam.
Look at the flowers in the spring,
Look at the happiness the summer brings.
Look at the buds, they're sights to see,
Look at the blossom on a tree.
Look at the golden autumn rays,
And remember forever on darker days.

Holly Rose Louise Heath (10)
Napier County Primary School

THE BOOK OF LIFE

You open up a book when you are born,
The first page - white as snow.
The book that is opened is your book of life,
Which you will fill with love.

Your book is quite full now,
With tears, jokes and fun.
Nearly full now,
But you can still go on.

One more page left to fill,
You are old and grey.
Getting tired and sleepy now,
You'll soon be on your way.

Your time has come for you to go,
Your book is now full up.
With memories and family,
That you were there for once.

Your book is in an angel's hand,
Held close to her heart and dear.
It will be put in a chest
And it will be left for you to read when you feel fear.

Another book is opened,
A new life in the world.
A new page to write on,
A new book to fill up!

Nicola Codling (11)
Napier County Primary School

WITCHES

Witches could be thin or fat they
sometimes wear a wig or a black
pointy hat. They have pets like frogs
and dogs and snakes that bite.
Witches also make cats chase rats which
will give you a fright.

Dead-man's toes and witches hats, frogs legs
and big black cats - long nails
and puppy dog tails.

Witches cast a spell on crocodile's
tails and on long nasty slimy snails.
Also witches have long green nails which
will remind you of hell.

Dead-man's toes and witches hats, frogs legs
and big black cats - long nails
and puppy dog tails.

Witches fly on broomsticks they stir
up trouble in the pots that bubble.
Witches give you a fright in the
middle of the night. Also they go around
playing dirty tricks.

Now I have come to the end, so listen
up my friend. Hope you liked my witches poem
which will make you scream, goodnight and
pleasant dreams!

Govinda Singh Bhakar (11)
Napier County Primary School

THE MIDNIGHT FOX

In the darkness of night the fox
swayed in the wind,
Like a skyscraper in a gale.

Her black fur dancing with the wind.
She was a black furred fox.
Camouflaged,
On the stroke of midnight.

The fox was invisible
When she swiftly pounced in and out,
Of towering verdant dales.
She faded into the dark, black woods.
As the night grew older and the darkness
grew thinner,
She crept slowly back to her home
Not making a sound.

Nadine Wheeler (9)
Napier County Primary School

THE NEW YEAR

To the millennium and beyond,
One of which we will all be fond.
The one night in the year
There was merriment and cheer.
The world celebrated all over
From Sydney Harbour to
The corner shop barber.
America - one of the last to share
In the wonderment of a fantastic
Start to the New Year.

Alice Childs (8)
Napier County Primary School

THE STRANGE PIG

I sailed to an island
Where there lived a pig
That always did a jig.

There was a ring in his nose
He must have liked it, I suppose!

He had a curly tail
And his face was very pale.

He had hairy arms
And tattoos on his palms.

As for his tummy
It was smothered with honey.

He had a dog called Fergie
But I think it had the lurgy.

As for the dog
It became a frog.

I couldn't stand it anymore,
I sailed away like never before.

Kylie Newport-Dempster (11)
Napier County Primary School

THE MILLENNIUM

The new millennium is another chapter to a big story,
but this is not any ordinary story.
Another day is another page.
We read each word by living our lives.
This is a book we cannot put away,
we have to read on and on.

In the last chapter all the inventors around the world
have changed how we live.
Thanks to Alexander Graham Bell communicating is
as easy as one, two, three.
Thank you to the Wright brothers.
We can now see the aerial view of the country.
The same thanks to the Montgolfier brothers -
but they found a way to take to the sky by using hot air.

Emmeline Pankhurst after chaining herself to some railings
achieved rights for women.
Florence Nightingale
Martin Luther King had a dream - and so do I.
I dream that everyone is treated equally
Young and old
Men and women
Black and white
No matter what colour or creed
No matter what you believe.
Everybody is the same and so that is how we all should be treated.
All these people are my heroes.
Read the pages through and through.
What heroes are there here to you?

Florence Edridge (9)
Napier County Primary School

MIDNIGHT WITCH

The clock has struck twelve - midnight is here,
The witch is on her broomstick, with a sinister leer.
Trouble is brewing at the edge of town,
And the witch is steadily flying down
A deep, wide cauldron with deep purple potion.
The witch is stirring it in a moon-shaped motion.
'Children! Children, come to the barman!'
Children, not amused by the witch's voice,
They carry on spreading marzipan.
The sun is slowly rising from its cloud-like bed,
The witch is flying home to her bare, clotted shed.
Until another night, may the witch rest?

Phoebe Troy (8)
Napier County Primary School

TWO LITTLE RABBITS

A little brown rabbit popped out of the ground
Wiggled his whiskers and looked around
Another little rabbit who lived in the grass
Popped his head out and watched him pass

Then both the little rabbits went
Hoppity hop, hoppity hop, hoppity hop
Until they came to a wall
And had to stop

Then both the little rabbits
Turned themselves around
And scuttled off home
To their holes in the ground.

Debbie Charlton (10)
Napier County Primary School

MERINGUES

Little clouds of pink and white
Sitting on my plate,
They're all sweet and sugary
I think they are just great!

I would have them for dinner
I would have them for tea,
I would have them for breakfast
But my mummy
Won't let me!

The little clouds of pink and white
Were sitting on my plate,
But now they've disappeared somewhere
I think they tasted
Great!

Rosie Bannister (10)
Napier County Primary School

FLYING SQUIRREL

He sails through the air with a natural grace
It seems that he's got a smile on his face
He pulls up - just in case!

At last he gets to the top of the tree
He didn't know what he would see
Suddenly he calls to me.

Ian Matthews (8)
Pembury Primary School

FLYING HIGH

I'm a bird flying high in the sky,
And the higher I fly,
The more I fry,
And if I get too close to the sun,
I'm sure it wouldn't be nearly as much fun!
I flap my wings to help me glide
Keeping as low as I can
So I won't get fried.
And because of the sun,
I fly into a tree,
Then a few minutes later I set myself free.
I fly into a tree,
Because of my sweat
Or sometimes to stop me from getting wet.
In the winter I don't get to wear a hat,
some boots or even a glove.
So sometimes I wish I had a coat like a dove.

Jonathan Anstey (9)
Pembury Primary School

SNAKE

You can see her different coloured bands
She slithers through the sand
She lives in a foreign land.

She spits her deadly poison out
She's scaly and deadly all about
Her scaly pattern's like a trout.

Oliver Hall (9)
Pembury Primary School

TREES

Thick brown trunk
My arms can't stretch around it
The thick dark green leaves hide the sky
Big Ben goes tick-tock, the trees hide the clock.

The holes in the trees where squirrels live
Where the crooked branches in spring
All nice and bare the trees are
Just like fingers and fingernails.

The leaves go sway, sway, flying in the sky
The wind blows on them
Then they go around the tree,
Flying around - up, up and down.

Emma Julie Henson (8)
Pembury Primary School

THE BUTTERFLY

Flitter, flutter goes the butterfly
So swift and graceful does he fly
So quiet
So peaceful
So colourful too
So fragile is the butterfly.

Lauren Beeching (8)
Pembury Primary School

MY DOG BART

My dog Bart runs around my garden
Not stopping until he gets food
As he goes again
Running about the garden
Comes indoors, gets mud everywhere.
Comes into the living room
Jumps on my brothers and me.
He eats all the food we have dropped on the floor.
He's like a Hoover.
Never stops eating until he has gone to sleep.
There he lays, silent as ever,
Not even a bark from his mouth
When he wakes up - he starts again.

Callum David Rennie (9)
Pembury Primary School

THE KINGFISHER

He lies on the rocky stick and he sweeps down
He swoops to catch his prey - down he swoops
He swept down, swooping across the skies.

He drops once more to catch the falling fish
King of the seas, diving down for fish to eat
He dives for water to drink and food to eat.

Rory Gilbert (9)
Pembury Primary School

MY MILLENNIUM POEM

Boom, whizz, popping, crackling
These are the sounds of the millennium dawning.

Reds, blue, green and yellow
These are the colours my eyes are seeing.

Smoky, burning, sizzling smells
These are in my nose as well.

What does the millennium mean to me?
A future of uncertainty!

A world full of happiness would be nice
What would we need to sacrifice?

Jack Vaughan
Pembury Primary School

MONKEYS AND DOLPHINS

Monkeys play in the dark green leaves
While cheeky ones play in the trees
Eating bananas by the deep blue seas
The cheeky, greedy monkeys.

Dolphins play with each other
By the squeaking of their mother
As the little girl plays with her brother
While all of them watch each other.

Sarah Hendley (8)
Pembury Primary School

My Cats

Ginger is
the colour of marmalade,
soft and fluffy,
with huge green eyes.
He loves to doze on my bed.

Oscar is a tom cat.
He is a mischief maker
with large beady eyes.
If you start to shout at him
he cocks his head to one side.

Floss is velvety, cuddly,
black and white.
Eyes like saucers,
full of surprise.
She enjoys scrambling up tall trees.

Joanna Curry (8)
Pembury Primary School

The Bat

Bats come out at night
And give everyone a fright.
People are in bed
Bats are outside instead
Hanging upside down
And squeaking through the night
And someone gets a fright.

Craig Waters (9)
Pembury Primary School

ANIMALS, ANIMALS, ANIMALS GALORE

Animals, animals, animals galore
Rabbits that jump
Birds that fly
Bees that sting you in the eye.

Animals, animals, animals galore
Snakes that hiss
Creatures that crawl
And giraffes that have long necks
And are tall.

Emma Newton (9)
Pembury Primary School

ANIMALS

Fishes swimming in the sea,
Guinea pigs on your knee.
See the rabbits in the hutch,
See the mice they don't do much.
Watch the hamster in his wheel,
See the cat with the cotton reel.
Hear the parrots they always squawk,
Must take the dog for a walk.
See the zebras they have stripes
The elephant trunks look like pipes.
Giraffes' necks are very long,
The birds sing a lovely song.

Katy Shelton (8)
Pembury Primary School

THE WINTER'S DAY

It was bright when I woke up
Everything was dazzling white
I saw snowflakes falling softly from the sky
And frosty patterns on my window.
'It's snowing!' I shouted excitedly.
Outside the glistening snow was crisp and deep on the ground,
The trees were decorated with sparkling white snow,
Everything was still and quiet.
I saw icicles hanging from rooves - sharp as knives
And a robin perched on the fence,
Shivering, his red breast bright and fluffy.
In the park the silver lake was frozen, glistening in the sun.
A duck stepped on the ice and slipped in surprise.
I took my sledge and whizzed down the hill,
Scarf flying behind me, my cheeks all rosy.
The chilly wind blew and my breath was cold.
We ran in the snow, our boots crunching, making footprints,
We threw snowballs at each other, laughing happily.
My fingers and toes began to feel numb.
Time to go home to get warm by the blazing fire.

Laura Masters (9)
Pembury Primary School

SNAKE

Slivery and slimy down the road
Noisy rattle all the way
Around the world in ninety days
Keeping out of everyone's way
Eating the livestock
Yum, yum, yum - now I've got a big fat tum.

Kevin Everest (9)
Pembury Primary School

I'VE WON THE LOTTERY

I've just won the lottery
But I'm not going to tell my mum.
There's millions in the bank and I'm going to have some fun.
I'm going to buy a bike and a trip to Disneyland.
I'm going to buy some drums and set up a good band.
My band likes to travel so we're going on holiday.
This year it is Brazil where we're going to sunbathe all day.

Next it's off to Egypt with the giant pyramids.
I hope we find a tomb of the pharaoh who once lived.

Then back to England and I'm going to tell my mum
But my friend had done the job for me
So she went *wild with fun.*

Harvey Green (9)
Pembury Primary School

THE PENGUIN

The penguin likes the cold
His beak is shiny gold
And waddles in the Antarctic - I've been told!

His black and white body is shiny
He once ate a fish that was very slimy
The fish was very scaly and liney.

Clare Richards (8)
Pembury Primary School

Thank Goodness It's Friday

At five to nine the children come in
ready for their work to begin.

Noisily the children work
making the teachers go berserk.

At half-past ten assembly time
after that it is just fine.

Now it's time to work again
Literacy hour - always the same.

Teachers are recovering from a busy morning
all the children now tired and yawning.

Numeracy hour makes the children work hard
leaving teachers with more books to mark.

Every child impatient they can't wait
Golden Time is now five minutes late.

Today the time has passed so slow
but now it's time for them to go.

Mum is waiting at the gate
she hopes the children won't be late.

Thank goodness it's Friday
tomorrow I can play!

Kelly Heath (9)
Pembury Primary School

THE TINY FLOWER

I am a tiny flower,
I stand here every day
as lonely as can be.
I'm all alone I have no friends
right here in this big park.

I am a tiny flower,
everyone treads on me.
No one is ever careful
I love it when it rains,
it's really, really fun.

I am a tiny flower
and when the sun shines bright
I grow so tall.
I reach up to the sky
growing stronger each day.

I am a tiny flower
I'm really nearly dead.
No more sun for me to grow,
no more tiny flower.

Lucy Rudge (8)
Pembury Primary School

WINTER POEM

W hite soft snow.
I   cicles hanging down.
N   orth wind howling.
T   emperature drops below zero.
E   verything glistening silver.
R   oll on spring.

Lydia Burgess (9)
Pembury Primary School

THE SOIL OF THE EARTH

The rain soaks into it and gardeners and ducks are pleased.
Roots of fragrant flowers grow into it and drink its water.
Farmers grow fields of crops to feed our families.
We dig through its layers, making foundations to hold our
buildings up straight.
Hard working miners dig for coal and gold.
Millions of feet walk on it and rivers flow across it
all night and day.
Girls and boys play It and chase all over the
little blades of grass.
We camp on it making lots of holes in the soft green turf.
Badgers build setts, moles make tunnels and foxes dig dens.
Rabbits work their warrens in it and dogs bury juicy bones
but forget where they left them.
Long wiggling worms feed on it and make their curly casts.
Dead people are buried in it in peaceful cemeteries.

Arthur Mazzey (9)
Pembury Primary School

TROUBLESOME PETS

Our tabby cat and collie dog always chase each other.
They run around, knock things down and quite annoy my mother.
If you stroke my tabby cat, he hisses but does not purr,
He gets out his claws, backs away and raises up his fur.
My hamster loves to eat and also loves to bite!
One day I put my hand in his cage and he gave me quite a fright.
The other day I lost my rabbit, so I wrote upon a board,
'Missing, one large rabbit, but only one small reward.'
The only one that is no bother is my guinea pig who lives in a hutch,
She runs around and sniffles, but doesn't do very much!

Jessica Woodgate (9)
Pembury Primary School

TREES

Trees, trees,
look how tall they grow -
when will they stop, does anybody know?
Trees in autumn are a colourful delight
with their golden leaves gleaming, what a splendid sight.
The golden leaves turn to red
like nice sweet red cherries on a clear summer's night.
Trees in winter are bare and boring.
I hear them calling, *swish-swosh, swish-swosh.*
Trees in spring come to life.
I see their fresh green leaves shooting upwards to the light.
Trees in summer shade you from the scorching sun.
I sit down watching the blossoms fall one by one.

Trees, trees,
what a wonderful sight.

Stephanie Dunn (8)
Pembury Primary School

LITTLE BROTHER

I have a little brother
he's really like no other.
He'll talk and talk and talk
and he'll always run not walk.

He has sticking-up hair
and he'll always do a dare.
He drives me mad at times
but I'm very glad he's mine.

Lauren Fitzgerald (8)
Pembury Primary School

WINNIE THE WONDER DOG

My dog is a treasure in our lives
She'll live for many years.
She runs through fields of golden corn
With soft flapping ears.

She pulls so hard on her lead
To get to where she's going.
We throw her ball for her to chase
And still she keeps on flowing.

In winter she sleeps by the fire
To have a little nap.
Sometimes she comes over to us
And sleeps upon our lap.

When she steals my toys and clothes
She hides herself in secret.
She won't come out and give them back
Until she has a treat.

Even if she gets into mischief
We still love her a lot.
She keeps us fit and makes us laugh.
Winnie's the best dog we've got.

Adam Merrin (9)
Pembury Primary School

UP, UP AND AWAY

U p in the sky planes zoom by.
P arachutes gracefully drop down.

U p float colourful hot air balloons,
P eople wave happily from the swaying basket.

A stronauts look down on our tiny world.
N oisy helicopters whizz through the clouds.
D ancing butterflies dance through the air.

A nd birds soar high over treetops.
W indy blustery days bring out bright kites.
A mazing shuttles shoot up into space.
Y es, the sky is not quite so peaceful.

Elizabeth Drapper (8)
Pembury Primary School

THE COUNTRYSIDE

The countryside has trees,
birds, flowers and bees.
A farmhouse on the hill,
nearby a windmill.
The bees collect pollen
from all the flowers.
To them they look
as tall as towers.
Birds build their nests,
high up in the trees.
They weave in and out,
with twigs, mud and leaves.

Ross Bromley (8)
Pembury Primary School

MY FIRST FLIGHT

My first flight
was a very big fright.
Although I thought it was fun.

When I got on the plane
I had to walk along a lane
and I sat in the seat at the front.

I saw a bolt of lightning.
It was quite frightening
as I looked out the window below.

It was very high,
with clouds in the sky
as the storm began to blow.

It was scary
so I was wary
as I said 'This is your pilot speaking!'

Matthew Rice-Tucker (9)
Pembury Primary School

TIGGER

There once was a cat called Tigger.
He always worried about his figure.
He lived down my road
And once caught a toad.
Oh how I loved that sweet little Tigger.

Les Chaffe (8)
Pembury Primary School

MY CAT JIM

My cat Jim is as bold as brass,
as silently he creeps through the long green grass.
Steady as a rock he crouches and waits,
he's seen next door's cat come over the gate.

As slow as a snail he gets ready to move,
to show who's boss he's going to prove.
As fast as a bullet, quick as a flash,
the other cat sees him, they're going to clash.

Hissing and spitting their eyes draw level,
the other cat turns and runs like the Devil.
Back over the gate to the safety of its house,
our garden again is as quiet as a mouse.

My cat Jim is as bold as brass,
as he licks his paws in the long green grass.

Luke Hattle (9)
Pembury Primary School

HAMSTERS

H oney-coloured hamsters
A wake every night.
M unching mini-mountains of nuts,
S tuffing their pouches full of food.
T wisting and tugging at the sides of their cages,
E veryone's favourite pet.
R unning aimlessly round and round in their wheels,
S queaking and squealing for a chat with me.

Sarah Tollefson (8)
Pembury Primary School

IMAGINARY POEM

Some children like to imagine things,
Pretending they're princesses, queens or kings.
Hoping that money will soon grow on trees
Saying all this in twos or threes.
They sometimes say, 'I'm a pop star today.'
Still saying this when they're old and grey.
Boys like to say they're a football star
Playing in countries near and far.
People with whiskers or maybe a tail
In a shop they see a big fat whale.
Have magical powers if they say a short rhyme
Lasting forever 'til the end of time!

Emma Shiel (10)
Perry Hall Primary School

I WOULD LIKE

I would like a cat to stroke and play with.
I would like a rabbit to hop around a cage.

But most of all I want my best friend back.
I would leave a cat or a rabbit if I could have my best friend back.

I get lonely now she has gone, it just is not the same without her.
I just wish I had my best friend back, that is all I want.

Hope Watson (9)
Perry Hall Primary School

PICTURES

Wouldn't it be great if we could pain a picture,
But not an ordinary picture,
A picture beyond your wildest dreams,
A picture you could step into.

You could paint a theatre,
With a band playing jazz,
While everyone sings,
To the wild, wacky sound.

Or go on a holiday to Barbados,
With its soft sandy beaches,
And the hot, red sun,
Shining all day.

Yes it would be great if we could paint a picture,
But not an ordinary picture,
A picture beyond your wildest dreams,
A picture you could step into.

Abbi MacAllister (9)
Perry Hall Primary School

THE MILLENNIUM BUG

The Millennium Bug is
round and fat,
blue and green,
wet and sunny,
isn't that funny.

It blocks up computers
that makes people fuss.
It jams up ticket machines
when you're on a bus.

The Millennium Bug is
round and fat,
blue and green,
wet and sunny.

Do you think that's true?
Mmmmm . . . let me think
I think it's funny.

Kristi Cormack (8)
Perry Hall Primary School

TEACHERS

Teachers teach us,
Teachers good and bad,
Teachers kind and gentle,
Teachers scatty and nervous;
Teachers confident and uncertain,
Teachers organised and disorganised,
Teachers extremely nice and funny;
Teachers strict and mean,
Teachers with no trust or sense of humour;
Teachers erratic and kind,
Teachers funny, strict and reasonable;
Teachers mean, weird and spiteful,
Teachers reactive and angry,
Teachers stressed out with difficult students!
Teachers stressed out with difficult parents and bosses;
Teachers doing their very best,
For so many different kinds of students;
Teachers after all, are like all of us,
Human beings too!

Charmian Oakes (10)
Poverest Primary School

MOBILES, FAGS AND MESSY STUFF

Mobiles are everywhere from France to Australia,
While fags just reek.
Chewing gum is in every crevice
And bubblegum is all over every kids' mush.
Rubbish is worse by far, it gets on animals,
Attacks fresh air and it's not blooming fragrant either!
So all litter louts are nuts, eh?
Mobiles bleep, fags stink, chewing gum and bubblegum are sticky,
    rubbish is evil.
To add to this ludicrous list, animal mess is dirt!
(No offence to animals or smokers).

James Cresswell (10)
Poverest Primary School

MY DANCING POINSETTIA

Red petals and berries
Green leaves so proud,
As it dances to the music
For the large Christmas crowd.
The velvet petals twist as it goes
And everybody gets excited
And hopes that it snows.
My dancing poinsettia does not thrive
On earth in the pot
But runs on batteries
That really make it rock.

Katie Norman (11)
Poverest Primary School

THE SEA

The waves are crashing on the shore;
They return again and crash once more.
The sun shines down on the shimmering sands,
Little children build sandcastles with their hands.
People splashing and having fun.
Others lying in the sun.

People with ice-creams are a common sight -
Seagulls swoop down to take a bite.
Deep-sea divers brave and bold,
See the mysteries of the deep unfold.
As the sun sets low once more,
The waters lap gently on the shore.

Christopher Miles (11)
Poverest Primary School

THE GRIBBLEY

I have a Gribbley
He's under my bed
He has fourteen eyes,
But only one head.

He nibbles the leftover stuff
Like biscuit crumbs, sweets and fluff.
He makes no noise, just like a mouse
But he frightens my sister out of the house.

Ben Howard Shearn (10)
Poverest Primary School

MY LOVE NIGHTMARE

I want to squeeze you tight,
Just like I did last night.
You used to be mine,
I'm running out of time.
You're getting on that train,
I think I went and lost my brain,
I've totally gone insane.
You asked me if I trusted you,
I said, 'Yes,' and asked if you trusted me too.
I guess it was a lie,
I feel like I should die;
You walked out that door,
Everybody saw,
You are gone . . .

Vanessa Thurgood (10)
Poverest Primary School

MILLENNIUM

The new millennium is here;
The time is now - I hear a cheer!
Fireworks, parties, masses of fun;
In two thousand years how far have we come?
Electricity, gas, even mobile phones!
Cars, pollution, don't forget The Dome.
Cars and computers,
Rush-hour and commuters!

But where will we be in the next thousand years?
No more wars, no more tears!

Sarah-Jayne Gibbs (11)
Poverest Primary School

I HATE POEMS

I hate poems,
They are dumb.
I hate poems,
And I can't write one.

I hate poems,
They must rhyme,
I can think of better things,
To do with my time.

I hate poems,
I don't know what to do,
When it comes to writing one,
I don't have a clue.

I hate poems,
They make me feel a fool,
I really don't know why,
Because they are quite cool.

I hate poems,
They drive me round the bend,
And now this verse is written,
I finally reach the end.

Jack Fawcett (10)
Poverest Primary School

GROWING UP

Screaming baby in his cot,
What a racket! Will he stop?
Mother moaning, rubbing her eyes,
She wakes up hearing the little cries.
Heating his bottle, mashing his food,
Baby won't wait, he's not in the mood.
A splash in the bath, a change of his nappy,
Mum will do anything to make him happy.
It's fun to watch him play and crawl,
Before you know it he'll be at school.
Growing up far too quick,
It's strange how he learns every trick.
Getting older, growing tall,
Seems only yesterday that he was small.

Rachel Darby (10)
Poverest Primary School

THE PHANTOM OF THE SKY

Every night in the sky
I see the phantom go by.
I wonder if he'll go away,
Because if he did I would say,
'Phantom of the night,
Be my shining light,
Till dusk, till in the morn.'
I wonder why you fly in the sky
While you shimmer in the night?
The moon shines bright while
You're in sight, stay with me
Through the night.

Cassey Gaywood (10)
Poverest Primary School

MY TEACHER

She is mean,
But usually keen,
Sometimes in-between!
She is tall, upon her stall,
And shouts at me loudest of all!

She is horrible to us all,
Just because we're all so small!
Most of all she is nice,
She is just like sugar and spice.

She works us hard, as hard as can be,
And keeps on at me!
And this is why you can see
I'm as clever as clever as can be!

Jenny Bassett (11)
Poverest Primary School

STONY BEACHES

Stony beaches are good fun,
There's lots to do for everyone.
Rocks and cliffs are some features,
Sea horses and crabs are some creatures,
Hear the waves crashing,
See the children splashing,
The sea never stops,
Children licking lollipops.
Kites flying high,
Watch the seagulls as they fly.
The crackling sound of pebbles being washed to shore,
I can't wait to go back for a little bit more.

Cathy Alcoran (9)
Poverest Primary School

WHAT SHALL I DO?

It's Monday night, what shall I do?
It's six o'clock on Monday I think I'll turn on the TV.
What's on?
I look in the TV guide and The Simpsons are on.
I'll watch The Simpsons.

It's Tuesday night what shall I do?
It's eight o'clock and I don't know what to do.
I know I'll read a book. What book shall I read?
I'll read Harry Potter, that's what I'll read.

It's Thursday night and I've just finished reading Harry Potter
So what should I do?
I know, I'll see what's on TV
I look in the book,
There's nothing much on.
So I'll just have a snooze.

It's Friday at last and it's nine o'clock sharp.
I turn on the TV for my favourite programme:
My favourite programme is Friends.
Normally straight after Friends is South Park,
I watch that as well.
It's ten o'clock what should I do?
I'll go up to my bedroom and lie on my bed,
Before I know what I'm doing I'm asleep.

Tara Short (10)
Poverest Primary School

SUMMERTIME

The sun it shines in the sky
I look above and wonder why
It shines so bright and feels so hot?
What a wonderful summer we have got.

The grass is green
And the flowers look nice
It's getting so hot
I could do with some ice.

The sky's so blue
And my skin is so brown
I would stay at the seaside
And not in the town.

As the sun goes down
The sky turns dark
What a wonderful summer we have got!

Natasha Sweetlove (11)
Poverest Primary School

THE SECRET CABINET

'Where is the secret cabinet Mum?
It could be something near the sun.
Can we go there, please, oh please?
I'll even get down on my knees.
I'll beg you at noon, from Monday to Friday,
Me and you can go swim near the bay.
Please, oh please, let me see the cabinet,
I'll even play my most dreaded game of,
Fish You See From Above.'

John Parker (10)
Poverest Primary School

THE LONELY BEAR

I am a lonely teddy bear,
Sitting on a shelf,
My friends and family have been sold,
So I am left here by myself,
My only friend is Panda,
But on Sunday he will be gone . . .
He is on reserve and happy,
But once more I will be alone,
People never pick me
And I often wonder why,
Is it because I am big and brown
Or because I have green eyes?
But wait - here comes a little girl,
She says she's looking for a bear,
She is coming straight towards me
And she clambers on a chair.
Her name is Alice Frome,
Alice plucks me from my shelf
And takes me to her home.

Lisa Daynton (9)
Poverest Primary School

THE CAT NEXT DOOR

The cat next door is very fat,
he's as dirty as a rat!
He wanders about looking for trouble
I'm so glad that there isn't double.

His body is covered in fleas
and he eats all of the mouse's cheese.
He scratches at his long scruffy fur,
I've never-ever heard him purr.

He has very big green eyes,
he uses them to seek out the flies.
His tummy is huge and round
but when he walks you can't hear a sound.

He eats lots of rubbish food,
and he is always in a bad mood.
The cat always sleeps under a tree,
he's happy to do it and does it with glee.

Chloe Mitchell (9)
Poverest Primary School

THE DREAM I WILL NEVER UNDERSTAND!

It's time for bed - the hour I dread,
I get so bored I think, 'Oh Lord
What am I meant to do now!'

Tonight it is different . . .
I'm starting to dream;
I am in a football team kicking the ball,
Suddenly down a big hole I fall.

I land with a thud into a pile of mud -
into the land of Noddy.

Suddenly I am being chased by a disgusting man with no face.
He chases me and I get caught - it isn't my fault.
He throws me on a trampoline -
I bounce into the stars - shiny and clean!
I come back down looking like a clown . . . great big red nose,
big shoes on my toes!
I can't take any more, I awake with a start;
And now I think I'd rather be bored!

Louise Fox (10)
Poverest Primary School

MY BIG SISTER

My big sister just bought a flat,
She keeps going shopping for this and that.
She bought new shoes and a coat,
Which looks like the skin off a goat.
She comes around every other week,
She opens the fridge and takes a peek.
Then Mum says, 'Would you like to stay for dinner dear?'

'No thank you, I'll have a beer.'
Then she grabs her coat and phone.
'See you Mum, I'm going home.'
As she walks down the street,
She thinks to herself, 'I should have stayed and had a treat.'

When she got home she could smell something nice,
It was her boyfriend cooking egg fried rice.

Laura Fitzgerald (10)
Poverest Primary School

CANDLES

Candles burning really bright,
Forever glowing in the night.
Always standing straight and tall,
Casting shadows on the wall.

Different candles you can buy,
Smelly ones for you to try.
Birthday ones I like the best,
And maybe some day I'll try the rest!

Light the wick and you will see,
Just how pretty they can be.
Orange, yellow burns the flame,
None of them are ever the same.

Nichola O'Neill (9)
Poverest Primary School

BRILL FOOTBALLERS

There was a brill footballer called Joe,
Thought he would put on a show,
When he got the ball,
He went past them all,
But his shot went off for a throw.

He walked up to the line,
A penalty - I must take my time . . .
Fell over a bump,
(That made him jump)
Caused a lump on his behind.

He missed the kick,
He took it too quick,
The keeper's hands waved,
He made the save,
Out of the cup,
Oh, how the team's sick!

Joe Hullett (10)
Poverest Primary School

MY LIFE

'I remember when you were born ten years ago
and when your mum was born, thirty years ago.
Now I'm one hundred and twelve years old.
Isn't that ancient?' said I.
'But Great, Great-Grandpa, why aren't you dead?' asked James.

'Well I remember when Mr Churchill came face to face with
Mr Hitler,' I said, 'and when England won the World Cup against
Germany in 1966, and I was there,' I continued, 'when Queen Victoria
handed the crown to her son in 1901 when I was thirteen.'
'Cool, how long have you lived in centuries?' questioned Jim.
'Mmm I wish you'd stop asking me questions. One century, one decade
and two years,' I replied, 'but my favourite time in my life was when
you were born.'

Edward Atkins (10)
St John's Primary School, Tunbridge Wells

OLD CLOCKS

Tick-tock goes the grandfather clock.
Old and worn, out of time.
The grandfather clock has a great chime.

Tick-tock goes the grandmother clock
Fragile and delicate, small but divine.
The grandmother clock keeps good time.

Thomas Hathaway (9)
St John's Primary School, Tunbridge Wells

Passing Of The Daytime

Get up at six o'clock,
Ready for school at seven.
After something to eat, run to school
Never early, never late.
Dad never up, when I'm at school.
Mum's running up and down the house.
Outside my dog is running around madly.
Teacher cross, I haven't got my homework
Homework has to be in tomorrow now 'good'.
Eating break at eleven o'clock
Run back in from break with Suzy.
Clock going faster, it's almost home time
Laura getting told off for kicking Jazz
Oh no, now Emma's late for maths
Clock's turning half-past three, 'yes'.
Kick the door, hooray, it's home time.

Madeline Smith (10)
St John's Primary School, Tunbridge Wells

Time Poems

Tick-tock time flies
My Nanny's dead, say goodbye.
If only I could turn back time
Everything would be fine.

Tick-tock went the clock
'It's time for bed' my mum said.
Not yet it's my favourite programme
I don't care it's 1am.

Edward Iles (9)
St John's Primary School, Tunbridge Wells

BEDTIME

Tick-tock, tick-tock
It is six o'clock.
Tick-tock, tick-tock
It is seven o'clock.
Tick-tock, tick-tock
It is eight o'clock.
Bedtime, bedtime
No!
It is eight o'clock
No!
It is eight o'clock
No!
Just five minutes more
No!
Just four minutes
No!
Just three minutes
No!
Just two minutes
No!
Bedtime always comes
Just like time comes and goes.

George Smart (9)
St John's Primary School, Tunbridge Wells

SUNDIAL

Sunshine makes a shadow.
Throwing a dark patch on a number cut into stone.
This idea didn't work
Even though it was a very good one.

The sun isn't out at night
So we had to find another way
To tell the time all the year
So we made a new invention called a clock.

Tamsin Prideaux (10)
St John's Primary School, Tunbridge Wells

THE YEAR 2000
(GRANDMOTHER CLOCK)

G et you it's a new millennium.

R eady for time travel?

A dawning of a new age.

N ew experiences ready for us.

D own here look I've got a hoverboard.

M onday, excellent, no school.

O nly weekends we go to school.

T he dog's a robot.

H and me the hovering toothbrush.

E nd of the 1900s no old-fashioned cars.

R obot cars you sit back and enjoy the ride.

C ool - isn't this new world, fantastic?

L ook at the telly, it's connected to the ceiling.

O ff we go upon the sofa.

C an we change channels?

K ick, isn't this great!

Joshua Breckman (9)
St John's Primary School, Tunbridge Wells

THE SUN

Hello Sun, nice to see you again.
Time after time I see your rays shining through my curtains
But why oh why is there not anything else,
Anything else to see?

Hi Sunshine, you're very bright, too bright for my liking.
Do you mind if I don't look at you directly
Because it will hurt my eyes immensely?

Howdy Sun, you're going now, here comes the moon.
Wait a minute, that's not the moon.
It's the eclipse, it's the eclipse, it's the eclipse!

Samuel Taylor (10)
St John's Primary School, Tunbridge Wells

GRANDMOTHER CLOCK

Tick-tock, tick-tock, goes the grandmother clock.
The grandmother sits by her clock, click-clack go the knitting
needles all day long.
Never-ever leaves her seat all day long, click-clack, click-clack.
Tick-tock, tick-tock, goes the grandmother clock.

Alistair Reynolds (9)
St John's Primary School, Tunbridge Wells

WHAT IS THE MILLENNIUM?

M ummy says I can stay up late.
I really don't know why.
L ittle me only goes to bed at eight.
L ike all my friends, but tonight I'm going to bed at twelve.
E laine says it's because Father Christmas is revealing himself.
N igel says it's because a giant fly is stuck on the sky.
N o, that's not true,
I think it's because it's a mill . . . mill . . . millenni
U m has passed.
M ummy says I'm right. Ha, ha, Nigel. Ha, ha Elaine,
                                             I'm right again!

James Bonner (10)
St John's Primary School, Tunbridge Wells

BIG BEN'S BELL

I am Big Ben's bell
I don't get what I have done wrong.
Why once an hour
Do I get tugged by my hair?
People like to hear me cry out in pain.
Twelve o'clock is the worst.
It happens twice a day
And I get twelve sharp tugs.

Mary Ward (9)
St John's Primary School, Tunbridge Wells

CLOCKS

I am a grandfather clock and I
Tick-tock, tick-tock.
I am a digital alarm clock
Tick-tock, tick-tock.
I am an analogue kitchen clock
Tick-tock, tick-tock.
I am a big, tall clock and I go
ding-dong, ding-dong.
I'm Big Ben so you had better block your ears.

Robert Wilson (10)
St John's Primary School, Tunbridge Wells

I CHIME

I chime, 1, 2, 3
But people just ignore me.
I chime, 4, 5, 6
What's the use of this?
I chime, 7, 8, 9, 10.
Oh there, looking at Big Ben
Now I chime 11 and 12
Wow! It's the next millennium
I feel important now.

Chloe Joyes (10)
St John's Primary School, Tunbridge Wells

SUMMER IS BEST

Rain on my window, rain in my face
Rain in the garden all over the place
Filling the bucket filling the pond
Soaking the gnome that never responds
I look up in hope for a crack in the sky
A ray of sunshine should never be shy
The grey clouds are tumbling and racing along
The wind is blowing and singing its song
My feet are now wet and my hands are cold
With my big coat around me, I look very old
I'm fed up with winter and its cold dark days
It makes it so miserable to go out and play
Now it's summer it's different, there's so much to do
When the mornings are light and the evenings too
The days seem much longer with plenty of time
To play in the garden with friends of mine
Shorts and T-shirts and nothing on our feet
Cold drinks to save us from the blistering heat
People are smiling and saying hello
Talking of holidays and where to go
Under the umbrella with plenty of cream
I look at the clouds and start to dream
That one's a bear that one's a rocket that one's a dragon
Letting off steam
There's no doubt about it, that summer is best
No hat, coats, gloves and winter vests
No colds and flu with plenty of bed rest
In summer I'm happy and healthy too
I feel so much better and full of fun
And all this is because of the warmth of the sun.

Hannah Jones (10)
St Katherine's School, Snodland

FIREWORKS

Zoom! Boom!
Flicker, flash,
Fireworks hit the air,
With an exploding *bash!*

Smoke is in the air,
Sparklers like a flare,
Gashy greens and glacier blues,
And colours that make you stare.

Blood-red, violent violet
Thunder-yellow,
Glittering gold, sizzling silver,
And rose-pink are in the air.

Sparklers, screechers,
Fountains, springs,
Bangers, Catherine wheels,
And rockets make a racket.

The bonfire night is nearly done,
We've had a lot of firework fun,
Yellow smoke has left the air,
And the fire's lost its last flare.

Benjamin Spencer Ashby (11)
St Katherine's School, Snodland

BONFIRE NIGHT

Along we go on to Bonfire Night
Oh what a wonderful, beautiful sight.
Fireworks going off all around,
Oh, so many different sounds.

Sparkling silver, gold and green,
Such a colourful exotic scene,
As sparklers begin to fizz and crackle,
I bite into my toffee apple.

Whiz go the rockets,
Soaring through the sky.
While we dig deep in our pockets,
For a penny for the guy.

As we leave the bonfire is still burning,
The last Catherine wheel has stopped turning
Everyone has gone home,
The smouldering guy is left alone.

Sam Baker (11)
St Katherine's School, Snodland

THE CROOKED OLD MAN

This is the story of the crooked old man:

Once there was a crooked old man,
Who walked a crooked old mile,
To find his crooked old son,
Then walked another crooked old mile,
Then he died with a crooked old smile
And that's the story of the crooked old man.

Emma Arbuckle (11)
St Katherine's School, Snodland

FIZZY FIREWORKS

Loud and scary fireworks,
Shooting up to Mars.
Then bang! They disappear,
In a sky full of stars.

Swishing, whooshing, whirring,
Fireworks all around.
Flashing, bursting, shooting high,
Then they hit the ground.

Violent violet,
And sulphur-yellow.
Make children scared,
And make them bellow.

When the fireworks are over,
And we say goodnight.
They set one more loud one off,
To give me a fright.

Aaron O'Shea (11)
St Katherine's School, Snodland

AN APPLE'S JOURNEY

It's nearly time to fall,
It's been coming for weeks.
I was getting myself prepared,
Then suddenly,
A gust of wind hit the whole tree,
Then I went tumbling to the ground,
The farmer came along,
Put me in a box,
The farmer put the box on a tractor.

On the tractor to the market,
There I was bought by a friendly vicar,
It's time for harvest,
All arranged in church,
It's time for giving,
Harvest festival.

Daniel Adams (11)
St Katherine's School, Snodland

BANG!

Wrap up warm with hats and scarves,
As it will be cold this night.
Burgers and jacket potatoes,
I'm looking forward to having,
I'm ready for Bonfire Night.

   Bang!

Bright flashes in the sky,
They explode like dragons' fire.
And splatter into sulphur yellow and violent violet
The screamers and the Catherine wheels
You see them shooting in different ways,
Don't forget the bangers!

   Bang!

Bonfires burn while people watch,
Sparks are everywhere.
Hear the twigs crackle madly,
Guy Fawkes burns to a cinder,
Everything just sizzles.

   Bang!

Jamie Pearson (11)
St Katherine's School, Snodland

MY BABY SISTER

I've got a baby sister,
Who's getting all the stuff.
She's got a thing with Barbies,
Because she makes a great big fuss.

I've got a baby sister,
Big, pink, ugly thing.
She's got these pyjamas,
They look like little wings.

I've got a baby sister,
She dribbles all over me.
She's got a thing with nappies,
She doesn't seem to wee.

I've got a baby sister,
She's only one year old.
I know this is funny,
But her head is going bald.

I've got a baby sister,
She gets bigger every year.
But the best thing is,
I love her very dear.

Elizabeth Lee (11)
St Katherine's School, Snodland

THE SHINING STAR

Twinkle, twinkle little star
Up above the sky so blue,
Shining down upon the Earth,
To make everything bright and true.

Alisha Jenner (10)
St Katherine's School, Snodland

FIREWORKS

Glowing brightly in the sky,
Sizzling, swirling way up high.
Popping, banging loud and clear,
Hissing, whizzing, sizzling for all to hear.

Rides to go on, people having fun,
Lots of sweets to eat like an iced bun.
Bonfire's grilling, flames up high,
People burning the bonfire guy.

Sausages, burgers scorching hot,
Great big bonfires with a guy on top.
Writing names with sparklers bright,
Catherine wheels glowing, twirling in the night.

Fireworks are finished, people go home,
For another year at the Millennium Dome!

Anthony Hunt (11)
St Katherine's School, Snodland

GORDON BANKS

Gordon Banks is the best,
He doesn't even wear a vest.
When he goes to play,
He saves the goals every day.
When he dives,
He saves everyone's lives,
Because he's Gordon Banks.

Jamie Denne (10)
St Katherine's School, Snodland

A HARVEST POEM

When mentioning harvest festival,
I begin to see,
All the starving kids in Africa,
Who depend on you and me.

All the donations our school gives out,
Show me how good it can be.
When harvest comes and we work together,
It is a chance we all should see.

To see the old people smiling,
All because we care.
And that everyone is happy,
Because at harvest we all share.

The donations of flowers,
The fact that we go out of our way.
Just to make sure that everyone,
Enjoys this special day.

Graeme Reigate (11)
St Katherine's School, Snodland

PARTY

Parties are fun, let's eat some more,
A few surprises,
Rolling about in bunches of people,
Tempting, tempting to roll some more.
Some parties are boring but this one isn't.
Let's play some more.
I think parties are great, especially this one.
Yawn! The end of the party.

Lisa Chapman (10)
St Katherine's School, Snodland

BOOKS

I open a book and read,
The chapters, page by page.
One chapter a unicorn,
A vampire next.
Without books life would be so dull,
And seconds would be like slowly passing hours.
Harry Potter and his adventures,
To Charles Dickens, A Christmas Carol.
Words produced like magic,
From the tip of a magician's wand.
Books are like pets,
One day alive in the mid-pages,.
The next, dead at the final paragraph.

Daniel Pepper (11)
St Katherine's School, Snodland

THE GHOST

I had a fright upon the night,
When the bedroom light was dim,
I lay there in my bed,
With my pillow on my head.
The curtains blew and then I knew,
It surely was a ghost.
Was it eating bread or was it eating toast?
Was it climbing a ladder or was it the lamp post?
Then the cat jumped in and woke me up,
To find I had been dreaming.

Philip Hayes (10)
St Katherine's School, Snodland

IT'S HARVEST TIME

Rosy-red apples,
Juicy green pears,
Waiting to be picked,
By the farmer.

Little green grapes,
Red fat tomatoes,
A little but bit worried,
About their new life.

Long, fat bananas,
Thin runner beans,
Trying to run away,
Never give up.

We should be thankful,
For what we have got,
Think of the others,
Who have nothing at all.

Charles Moore (10)
St Katherine's School, Snodland

PETS

I have a hamster who is *very* lazy,
I always think thank God I didn't call him Mazy,
Pets, why are they so tiring?
They're always sleeping.
Hamsters are quite small,
When they're climbing they sometimes fall,
My hamster is very small and white,
His eyes are so bright.

Georgina Nicolettos (9)
St Katherine's School, Snodland]

HARVEST

Corn:

Gleaming in the golden sunlight,
Swaying in the gentle breeze,
Standing straight to attention,
Turning pink with summer's eve.

Apples:

Hanging from the ladened tree boughs,
Like baubles on a Christmas tree,
Rosy-red, shiny faces,
Round in perfect symmetry.

Grapes:

Dripping from the leafy vines,
Like purple tears from green eyes,
Cascading, gleaming juicy bubbles,
Sway rhythmically with gentle sighs.

Yasmin Joyce (11)
St Katherine's School, Snodland

MY MONSTER

There's a monster called Ted,
He lives under my bed,
With warts on his nose,
And likes to nibble my toes.
He's ugly, big and fat,
And attacks next-door's cat.
He's really a pain,
But I love him for that.

Natalie Hornsbury (9)
St Katherine's School, Snodland

CHARLIE'S POEM

Charlie is a dog that's black,
He likes to bark and chase the cats.
He's scared of some other dogs,
And he likes to play and jump on logs.
He likes to play with his squeaky toy,
Life with him is such a joy.
For his dinner he has dog meat,
Then afterwards he comes to lick your feet.
When we take him out for a walk,
We dread it when he sees another dog, he goes ballistic.
But when he's really good and ignores the other dogs,
We think he's fantastic.
When he sleeps he sometimes snores,
When you give him treats he hands you his great big paws.
He's always begging for food off our plates,
We give it to him so he will stay our mate.
Charlie is my favourite pet,
No other dog is quite like him, I bet.

Jennifer Allen (10)
St Katherine's School, Snodland

PRETTY FLOWERS, HAUNTED HOUSES

Pretty flowers, red, blue and green,
Haunted houses black, grey spooky.
Pretty flowers growing short and long,
Waiting till the sun comes along.
Haunted houses moving slowly,
Up the rivers going roughly.
People shaking as they see the ghost,
From the haunted houses.

Stephanie Karen Andrews (9)
St Katherine's School, Snodland

SEASONS

Dawn birds singing,
The spring,
Beautiful blooming flowers,
The spring.
Birds having baths,
The spring.

Hot sunny days,
The summer.
Sandy, hot beaches,
The summer.
Ice-cold drinks,
The summer.

Windy cold day,
The autumn.
Golden-brown leaves,
The autumn.
Bare, brown trees,
The autumn.

Freezing dark days,
The winter.
Cold, icy lakes,
The winter.
Warm, sweet cocoa,
The winter.

Katherine Bungay (11)
St Katherine's School, Snodland

EVERYDAY LIFE

People all over the world
Die of hunger and thirst,
Maybe for once, we should put them first,
In everyday life they deserve.

I know some people don't care,
But we can if we share,
Our time and days helping the poor,
Will change their life forever more.

We should help the poor people
Who have died in the past,
And keep their life going,
And make it last.

Kirsten Murphy (10)
St Katherine's School, Snodland

THE FRUITY TUNE

All the cabbages sitting in a row,
The fruit and veg had to grow.
Beetroot, lettuces and cauliflowers,
Apples, plums and marrows sour.

Wheat grows steadily hour by hour,
Eventually we will turn it into flour.
All the food that we will be sharing,
The people who gave them, were very caring.

Robert Kingsbury (10)
St Katherine's School, Snodland

KITTENS

The kitten is a furry pet,
Who plays all day in the warm sun.
My kitten is newly born,
He plays with wool and has lots of fun.

Their little eyes peep out from under their fur,
Their miaow is a little squeak of happiness.
The garden is a giant adventure playground for them
They leap and twirl and rest with tiredness.

Kittens are lots of fun, their bright eyes twinkling,
Twinkling at the corner and just thinking,
That when their playtime is over,
They will be in a peaceful sleep, slowly sinking . . .

Into a dream.

Kym O'Shea (11)
St Katherine's School, Snodland

MY RABBIT

There is a rabbit call Thumper,
He is a very good jumper,
He twists and turns
And twitches his nose,
But his hutch never smells like a rose,
His coat is like velvet and
His eyes are sparkling and bright,
But you will have to watch out,
Because he'll give you a bite!

Charlotte Hill (9)
St Katherine's School, Snodland

SNOW

A thick white blanket,
Covering the lawn.
Waiting in the sky,
And falling down at dawn.

Lovely and soft,
On the ground.
So if you fall over,
You are safe and sound.

That means that you won't get hurt,
So believe what this poem says.
You are allowed in the snow,
Until the sun melts it with its rays.

The sun so hot and in the sky,
With lots of clouds surrounding it.
But watch out for when next, snow falls,
There will be snowball fights, yes, what a hit!

A thick white blanket covering the lawn,
Waiting in the sky,
And falling down at dawn.

Amy Lear (10)
St Katherine's School, Snodland

THE OLD LADY

The old lady in the rocking chair,
With grey and whirly hair.
Her face was wrinkled,
But her eyes still twinkled,
As if she were still young.

Luke Everhurst (10)
St Katherine's School, Snodland

SEASONS

The wind does blow,
It whispers through the trees,
Stirring and rustling,
The golden autumn leaves.

The sun is bright and hot,
Making the red brown and gold,
Of the autumn leaves,
Glisten in the light.

The snow gently falling,
A white blanket lays,
All around on the ground,
No animals making a sound.

Sara-Jaine Quinn (9)
St Katherine's School, Snodland

WAITING FOR SANTA

At night waiting for Santa,
It is as black as black smoke.
Outside not one thing moves,
Waiting for Santa.

Kids asleep waiting for Santa,
Clock strikes twelve o'clock.
Santa comes to my house,
Then your house.

In the morning me and you open our presents,
Then we go downstairs,
And what is down there, but presents!

Daniel French (10)
St Katherine's School, Snodland

MY TREE

There is a tree that I adore,
Every time I see it, I like it more and more.

It stands in the field behind our house,
It's probably the home of a squirrel or a mouse.

Its dark green leaves reach up to the sky,
I can't see the top, it goes so high.

The big brown branches stretch out all around,
And the leaves make a loud rustling sound.

I love that tree with all my might,
And hope it will always be in my sight.

Michelle Marie Rose (9)
St Katherine's School, Snodland

MY LITTLE SISTER

I put my little sister out with the rubbish,
And waited for the bin man to come.
Instead of taking her to the rubbish tip,
They gave her back to my mum.

I tried again but this time I put her in a bag,
And waited for the bin man to come.
Instead of taking her to the rubbish tip,
They gave her back to my Mum.

Fiona Worcester (10)
St Katherine's School, Snodland

YOU!

You!
Your head is like a bud.
You!
Your tears are like diamonds.
You!
Your belly is like a crystal ball.
You!
Your hair is like spaghetti.
You!
Your arms are like lamp posts.
You!
Your legs are like walking sticks.
You!
Your backside is like Snowdon.

Laura Anne Maynard (8)
St Katherine's School, Snodland

SOCCER

Soccer is good,
Soccer is great,
And if I go to play soccer,
I play it with my mate.
I support Man United,
The richest team in the league,
And if I ever go for it,
I'll always support that team.

Mathew Lewis (10)
St Katherine's School, Snodland

MY LITTLE GEL PEN

Here's my little gel pen
It's like a little friend.
It puts my words on paper,
And shows me what I've penned.

I've just had a thought,
It's really, really bad!
I love my little gel pen,
I think I'm very sad.

Oh well, I must stop dreaming,
And get on with my work.
I must remember it's just a pen,
I much prefer Captain Kirk!

Natalia Valerie Weaver (9)
St Katherine's School, Snodland

MY BUDGIE

My budgie,
My budgie,
With feathers so bright.
You hide in the trees in daylight,
You never come out in daylight,
Only at night.
Nobody sees but I know you're there,
I hear you chirping from my bedroom window,
Maybe I will see a glimpse of you one day.

Bianca-Caney Bryan (9)
St Katherine's School, Snodland

WWF Wrestling

WWF
Is so fun
I watch it every Sunday
I like it when someone wins
Especially Triple H.
I like it when my
Worst enemy had blood
And sweat coming out of him.
When Triple H loses
I always scream and shout
And stamp my feet.
I jump for joy and sing.
But the best bit is when
They all come in the ring
And get thrown out again.

Alice Chard (10)
St Katherine's School, Snodland

The Land Of Coo

In the land of Coo.
When the cow goes moo!
The dinosaurs go goo!
The Tyrannosaurus goes boo!
The Diplodocus goes coo!
The Charcharodontosaurus goes who!
That's how it goes in the land of Coo.

When the Syntarsus goes boo!
And the land goes *boom!*

Matthew Field (9)
St Katherine's School, Snodland

SOME DOGS

Some dogs are small and have pointed noses,
Some dogs like smelling sweet little roses.
Some dogs like playing with sticks and balls,
Some run away when their master calls.

Some dogs are fat and some are thin,
Some dogs are tall and can reach the bin.
Some dogs are lazy and sleep in their bed,
Counting the hours until they are fed.

Some dogs like going for a long country walk,
Some dogs like barking as if they can talk.
Some dogs are naughty and break up their toys,
Some dogs are girls and some dogs are boys.

Our dog's called Pixie, she's a Battersea dog,
She runs through the sun and runs through the fog.
She's funny, she's happy, she's a real Scooby Doo,
She likes talking to me and likes talking to you.

Holly Pepper (10)
St Katherine's School, Snodland

CHOCOLATE

Chocolate, chocolate all shapes and sizes,
Chewy ones, soft ones, full of delicious surprises.
The wrappers are shiny,
The nutty ones I hate,
The fudgy ones, I think are the best,
I think that they are great.
Chocolate, chocolate, I could eat it all day,
So *no one* dare take my chocolate away!

Michael Smith (10)
St Katherine's School, Snodland

SPIDERS

Spiders, spiders make my mum scream,
In our house she doesn't want them seen.
Spiders can be very small
Mum gets scared when ever they crawl.
If one crawls along beside her,
She quickly moves before it frightens her.
All the spiders think it's very funny
To scare my frightened, frightened mummy.
I don't care what you or they say,
All I know is that
Spiders, spiders
I love spiders.

Nicola Stevens (9)
St Katherine's School, Snodland

SHAPES

Shapes come round and square,
Big and small and any shape in the world,
They roll and roll but some of them don't,
Some are 3D and some are 2 which makes them flat.
Some are long and thin, tall and small.
Shapes are on the streets, on your faces and on the floor.
Some are even on the door,
Shapes are all around the world,
On the houses and the trees,
Some are even on me!

James Marshall (9)
St Katherine's School, Snodland

CHOCOLATE

I love chocolate,
I love eating lots.
I love it melted,
And I could eat pots and pots.

You can get it in packets,
In tubes and in bars.
And in all different shapes,
Like Milky Way stars.

Chocolate can be used,
In many different ways.
But you have to eat it quick,
Within a couple of days.

Otherwise it will melt,
Unless you keep it cold.
But if you keep it in the warm,
It will turn to yucky mould!

Sophie Carr (9)
St Katherine's School, Snodland

RAINING

Rain, it is coming,
And thunder and lightning.
In and out, all about,
Nothing can stop it.
It comes down like a rocket,
Now it has stopped,
Going and going finally down the drain.

Steven Prentice (9)
St Katherine's School, Snodland

MY MAD FAMILY

I have a little brother,
He is a little pain,
Every time I see him,
He makes me go insane.

I have a digging Dad,
Who is always building something,
No matter what he does,
He is down a ditch with nothing.

I have a short Mum,
Who has to admit,
When it comes to DIY,
She gets me to help her with it.

I have a white Westie,
She's as mad as me,
And she always licks my family
But anyway she is a good doggy.

Mum, Dad, my brother, my dog,
And me are such a mad family.

Joe Lemmon (10)
St Katherine's School, Snodland

SCHOOL

S   chool is fun
C   hildren running round
H   ome time is the best!
O   n my chair I sit and write
O   n the bell we go out to play
L   eaving is so tragic.

Sarah Martin (10)
St Katherine's School, Snodland

VALENTINE'S DAY

V alentine's Day has come
A boyfriend is what you need
L et them know that you love them
E ven if they don't love you.
N o one can stop you from giving them a present
T ick-tock we are waiting
I t's time to party,
N o one has had a party like a Valentine's Day party
E veryone is here,
S tart dancing everyone. Oh no! It's time to go.

D id everyone have to go home?
A ctually not everyone went home, but that's between
Y ou and me.

Georgina Bush (10)
St Katherine's School, Snodland

MR GOOFY

Goofy was mopping the floor
When he hit his head on the door.
He had a big lump on his head,
And so he stayed in bed.
He went on a bus,
And made a big fuss.
Goofy went to school,
To learn how to play ball.
He went in a football match,
And he got a catch!

Erika White (9)
St Katherine's School, Snodland

THE STRANGE MEETING

One day when I was little
A man came and said to me

'Egg, slap, splash, sugar, babe, fire'
So I replied, 'Spy go
Unlucky me!'

He turned me into a frog
Then a lump of butter,
He turned me into water
And I began to splutter.

He turned me back to human
Then he changed his mind
He turned me into a penguin
He wasn't very kind.

He turned me into a ball
Then rolled me down a hill
He thought he'd change me now
And turned me into a mill.

He finally turned me back
And I ran all the way home.

I cried and cried and cried
I shouldn't have, Mum was on the phone.

Sarah Bush (9)
St Katherine's School, Snodland

THE CAT THAT ATE THE HOUSE

Well, he started off as a normal cat
But that was all to change,
For Tiger was a monster
And a monster was he.

Well, he started off as a cute little thing
But cat's don't eat cushions, you see,
As Tiger was a mad cat
And a mad cat was he.

Well, he started off as a naughty little kit,
But he still had a liking for kebabs,
'Cause Tiger ate just anything
And anything he ate.

But one day, he went too far,
He gulped the whole house down,
You see Tiger was a crazy kit
And a crazy kit was he.

Well Tiger lived a happy life
And a happy life he lived
And when at last, he finally died
They put him in a museum.

Amy-Marie Dawes (10)
St Katherine's School, Snodland

BOYS

Boys are good at football,
Boys are good at baseball,
Boys are so cool,
Boys are good at fishing,
Boys are good at swimming,
Boys are excellent.
Boys are good at basketball,
Boys are good at pool,
Boys are magnificent.
Boys are good at a port,
Boys are good at sport,
Boys are brilliant.
Boys are good at snooker,
Boys are good at poker,
Boys are noisy.
Boys are good at getting dirty,
Boys are nearly thirty.
Boys are very tall,
Boys are very thin,
Boys are very fat,
Boys are aliens!

Sean Lear (9)
St Katherine's School, Snodland

RULES

It's Monday afternoon and it's nearly noon,
My ruler is bending and I am lending.
I got told off because I was being bad,
My teacher went mad.
I want to have a nap, but my ruler just snapped.

Laura Worcester (8)
St Katherine's School, Snodland

A TRIP TO WEMBLEY

It's the night before
I cannot get to sleep
I toss and turn in my bed
Thinking the clock will never bleep.

The day is finally here
I hope there is no catch
We leave to get the coach
To take us to the match.

When I get to Wembley
There's people everywhere
I have to find my seat
But there's plenty of time to spare.

The teams come out onto the turf
The crowd let out a roar,
Where's my favourite player?
He's wearing number four.

The match is very even
As both teams try to score
The balls crossed into the box
And up pops number four!

My team has won the cup!
I'm happy as can be
Now it's back to school on Monday
To face reality.

Joshua Simmons (9)
St Katherine's School, Snodland

MY MAGIC ROOM

In my magic room . . .
I will put my marvellous mum
My daft dad
My nutty nan
And wonderful Wendy.

In my magic box . . .
I will put my best cousin Ben
My bubbly best friend Bianca,
My accountant Aunty Tracy
And flying Uncle Richard.

My magic room . . .
Is made of silver and gold
With lots of jewels and is beautiful
I take it to the park
I take it to the beach
It is always with me
It is in my mind.

In my magic room . . .
I will put an end to the cruelty to animals
An end to all wars and human suffering
A cure for all diseases
And no more illegal drugs.

In my magic room,
I will put the feeling of chocolate melting in
My mouth
The weird feeling of going down the scenic railway
The fantastic feeling of swimming with dolphins
And the best feeling in the world - of being alive.

Sophie-Leanne Jeffery (9)
St Katherine's School, Snodland

OUR HEADMASTER

Our headmaster's office is small,
In it he plays with his ball,
But my teacher fell in love with him,
First she gave him a grin,
When she gave his a kiss,
She missed,
Our headmaster doesn't like mice,
Our teacher gave him some ice,
Our headmaster and teacher watched the moon
With its silver shine
Then in the middle of the night
They said 'Goodnight!'
My teacher turned into a frog
And our headmaster turned into a dog.

Jessie Bryen (8)
St Katherine's School, Snodland

SCHOOL!

I love school
It is really cool
I like maths
And English
But my favourite subject has to be
A little bit of
History!

Aimee Sutton (9)
St Katherine's School, Snodland

PLAYSTATION

P laying on the PlayStation is so much fun,
L earning all the moves when I've only just begun.
A chieving a new level is hard to do,
Y ippee! I've survived all the way through.
S uch concentration is on my mind,
T ogether, everything we will find.
A boss is coming very soon,
T hough I will shoot him to the moon.
I t's getting harder that the end is near,
O n I would go with frightful fear,
N ow it is completed I can give a big cheer!

Louis Sharp (10)
St Katherine's School, Snodland

ROMANTICNESS

How to be romantic . . . (For girls only)

Send some champagne and some wine,
That will make him have a good valentine.
Then some chocolates and ice-cream
So he can watch the football team.
Aftershave and gel will do the trick,
Shall I tell you my valentine's name? It's Nick,
Do you maybe suppose,
He might say yes if I proposed
First I need a big red rose.

Ashleigh Bungay (9)
St Katherine's School, Snodland

SWIMMING POOL

When our teacher blows the whistle
And she yells like a prickly thistle
She wastes her breath,
For I know what she's going to say,
'Guess what class, we've got swimming today,'
My mates say it's fun
But I say it's dumb
So into the slimy sub-zero water we go
And I just daydream then
'Are you there, hello!'
They push me in
Hey, I'm not a fish,
Where's my fin?
Yes! We're going
Schools in the past
And I'm at home at last!
My mum says I've got a surprise
How nice!
I'm going shopping after
So I'll get out my money tin
But the surprise is
I'm going for a swim!

Amber Price (8)
St Katherine's School, Snodland

PURPLE OLD SNAKE

There was a purple snake
That had a very bad headache,
He started to shake
And that was then end of the purple old snake.

Michael Ells (8)
St Katherine's School, Snodland

THE CONTEST

There's a contest at our school today,
I'm going to take part,
It takes place on first play.
On second play we'll have a rest,
We'll go inside
And have a maths test.
After school I'm gonna dance,
At our school disco 7 till 10,
Bob Walker just came back from France,
Harry Wales he drives me crazy,
Oh my gosh, he's given me a daisy
He's sweet and cuddly and really dishy,
Really unlucky Helga Smithy.

Lauren Jones (9)
St Katherine's School, Snodland

TEACHERS

My teacher wears purple satin pyjamas
And she likes eating peanut butter and bananas
She tells us off with a yell and a scream
She goes to the movies and watches the screen
And goes shopping the next afternoon.
At night she gazes at the twinkling moon
She cuddles up to her boyfriend
And starts a trend.

Naomi Randall (9)
St Katherine's School, Snodland

THE LOVELY TEACHERS IN MY SCHOOL

My English teacher is nice and polite,
She sits and eats Angel Delight,
She does not give us a fright.
My maths teacher is strict and polite,
She ticks our books at night,
She does not give us a fright.
My headmaster is strict and scary,
He does his work up in the office,
And he does give me a fright.

PS Be warned, he's very strict but nice.

Charlotte Harewood (9)
St Katherine's School, Snodland

SCHOOL!

School, school, school is great
Swing round the school gate
Play, play but the bell has gone
The sun is hot and it has shone.
Home, home I don't want to go home
The dog is in the school with a bone.
Catch, catch, catch that dog
Dog finds another dog and gives it a snog!
Now the school is going mad
And now Timmy is so sad
He got hit by a pen
And now Mrs Cook needs a fan.

Tony Payne (9)
St Katherine's School, Snodland

EVEN STEVEN

There is a boy called Steven,
He was always getting even.
He turned around and gave a smirk,
That's when he's getting even,
He's got even on his brother,
He got even on us that's what he did best,
Then some boys came round calling him names,
He got even on one and then the rest.
Then that boy called Steven did the biggest deed of all,
He jumped the fence, went across the yard followed by some boys,
They followed him nearly everywhere until they got worn out
And Steven was gone forever.

Steven Watts (8)
St Katherine's School, Snodland

MY BRILLIANT TEACHER

My brilliant teacher,
She likes wearing her long, blue skirt,
With her wonderful pink shirt.
She must have a massive wardrobe,
They always say,
And doesn't like the month of May,
But, of course I like her,
She's the best teacher in the school.
I like her singing in the hall.
It is now time to go home,
And do you know what?
She's my mum!

Emily Pullen (9)
St Katherine's School, Snodland

MY CRAZY TEACHER

I have a teacher who
Is very, very, silly.
A boy in my class called Billy,
He comes from Chile.
My teacher is crazy
And also very, very lazy.
I hate my teacher because
She says that I am always late.
She goes out with her mate
Called Kate.
I wish I had another teacher
That I will not hate.

Elizabeth Howick (8)
St Katherine's School, Snodland

TWISTER

Twister is a fast wind,
Twisters are like whirlpools,
Twisters are quite cool,
Twisters are very strong,
Twisters are fast,
Twisters are told to go by the weather forecast,
Twisters will blow you away,
Twisters are like a spinning top,
Twisters brake expensive pots.

Aaron Dawes (8)
St Katherine's School, Snodland

TEACHERS

Teachers are *bad*,
Teachers are *mad*,
They have big bellies,
They have names like Kelly.

They have scary faces,
They are so hairy,
Some are good,
They act like hoods.

They are crazy,
They are lazy,
Some are cats,
Some are bats.

Claire Moore (8)
St Katherine's School, Snodland

SCHOOL

School is mad
When I am sad,
But when I am glad,
I am hopping mad.
The teachers go bonkers
When we are throwing conkers.
Playtime is the best,
Because we get a rest.

Danielle Bishop (8)
St Katherine's School, Snodland

My Headmaster

My headmaster is blind,
But he is very kind.
He can be scary
Even though he looks like a fairy.
He can be batty,
Even when he's tatty.

My headmaster is crazy
Even though he's lazy.
He can be kind,
When he's got a good mind.

Max Lemmon (8)
St Katherine's School, Snodland

The Birthday Teacher

I have a teacher,
A teacher I have.
A birthday teacher I have,
She's very mad
And we're quite bad.
When it comes to your birthday,
The teacher goes mad,
And I am sitting here,
Very glad.

Victoria Rimell (9)
St Katherine's School, Snodland

You!

You!
Your head is like a bowling ball.
You!
Your eyes are like the holes in a bowling ball.
You!
Your nose looks like a pencil.
You!
Your mouth is like a banana.
You!
Your fingers are like sticks.
You!
Your belly is like a bowl of jelly.
You!
Your hands are like a piece of plastic.
You!
Your legs are like metal posts.
You!
Your hair is like spaghetti.

Thomas Edwards (8)
St Katherine's School, Snodland

Mike's Old Bike

There is an old bike which belongs to Mike,
Mike had this bike when Mike was five.
Mike's dad threw Mike's old bike away,
Mike's dad threw it far, it landed in a barn of hay.
Mike started crying and ran away,
He came back the next day.

William Smith (8)
St Katherine's School, Snodland

MR RABBIT

As I was walking home one day,
I saw something rather funny,
For hoping right in front of me
Was a little fluffy bunny.
I said 'Good afternoon Mr Bunny,
How are you today?'
And the bunny looked straight at me and said,
'Oh dear, I seem to have lost my way!'
I picked him up and stroked him
And told him where to go,
But whether he actually got there,
I suppose I'll never know.

Rachael Smith (9)
St Katherine's School, Snodland

WHIRLPOOL

Whirlpool swish, whirlpool swash,
Around in circles every day,
The same old way
Forever and ever,
Every way,
Every day,
You suck up boats,
Most of the time you swirl and swirl.
You must be hungry every day,
You eat everything in your way!

Joshua Adcock (8)
St Katherine's School, Snodland

THE HORSES

Fairy horses running through the grass,
Up and down the dusty path,
Eating carrots all day long,
Pulling along the open carts,
People eating red jam tarts,
On their way here from dancing class,
See the horses in the field
With some potato peels,
In the summer they're running around,
Up and down, jumping all around,
Then they will lay on the ground.

Kerry Morgan (9)
St Katherine's School, Snodland

THE SCHOOL POEM

Once I saw Mick and Mary
Snogging on the playground,
So Miss saw and sent
Them to headteacher.
Miss was disgusted
When she saw Louis was busted.
Then Jim Tonnie was crying on the railing,
After he got told off by Mrs Bailing.
Don't forget Miss Elwin
Got caught drinking beer in a tin.

Nicky Smith (9)
St Katherine's School, Snodland

THE FUTURE

Flying cars, no roadwork cones,
Shopping from home with hands free phones.
Maybe robot pets.
Clothes that don't need washing
And carpets that don't need hoovering,
That will be good for mums.
Grass that cuts itself
And cars that wash themselves,
That will be good for dads.
For us kids no homework or school dinners,
Just jelly and ice-cream and sweets.
Well, that's what I want our future to be like.

Nathan Lee (9)
St Katherine's School, Snodland

MY TEACHER

My teacher is very nice,
My teacher has six mice,
When people are very bad,
She gets really mad
And then that person is very sad.
My teacher is very nice,
My teacher has six mice.

PS Don't make her mad,
    or you will be very sad.

Amy Hobbs (8)
St Katherine's School, Snodland

YOU!

You!
Your head is like a blackboard.
You!
Your eyes are like houses.
You!
Your teeth are like ice-cream.
You!
Your legs are like fat trees.
You!
Your ears are as big as the sky.
You!
Your belly is like five fat men.
You!
Your fingers are just like a fat cake.
You!
Your mouth is full of worms.
You!
Your nose is as red as Mrs Stacy's face
                    when Mrs Stacy is angry.

Jessica Smith (8)
St Katherine's School, Snodland

DOGS

Dogs are nice,
They like mice,
I've got a dog
Who chases cats
And he sits on a mat.

Anne-Marie Forward (8)
St Katherine's School, Snodland

TEACHERS

There was a teacher who was very lazy
And was always being so crazy,
And sometimes they are bad,
And always very, very mad.
Most teachers are like a fairy
And the headmaster is so scary.
When the teachers are in the staffroom it's chatty
And their clothes are tatty.

Ryan Edwards (9)
St Katherine's School, Snodland

TEACHERS

I have a teacher, very smelly,
With a sticking-out belly.
I have a teacher like a bowl of jelly.
I have a teacher very clumsy and lazy.
I have a teacher and she is crazy.

Reece Cano (8)
St Katherine's School, Snodland

THE WHACKY TEACHER

There once was a teacher who had magical powers,
In the night she flies off to the towers.
The broom is brown, the broom is green,
She flies around making everything clean.

Sarah Seager (8)
St Katherine's School, Snodland

SUMMER

S ummer is fun and the sun is hot
U nder shades we must hide a lot
M aking castles in the sand
M usic coming from an ice-cream van
E very night the stars so bright
R ain, there's not a drop in sight.

Ben Miller (10)
St Katherine's School, Snodland

PLAYTIME

This boy was sad,
The other boy was bad.
He went to the teacher,
Then he wanted a creature.
He saw a plane crash,
Then he saw a car smash.

Luke Sterrett (8)
St Katherine's School, Snodland

FISHING

I like to go fishing,
Instead of just wishing.
I like to go fishing
Instead of mushy kissing.
I like to go fishing,
But don't tell Miss!

Kenny Randall (10)
St Katherine's School, Snodland

YOU

You!
Your head is like a hollow arm.
You!
Your fingers look like sausages.
You!
Your hair is like grease.
You!
Your belly is like a pocket.
You!
Your legs are like pieces of wood.

Ryan Maxted (8)
St Katherine's School, Snodland

YOU!

You!
Your nose is like a triangle.
You!
Your face is like a lined drum.
You!
Your bum is like a big apple.
You!
Your arms are like sticks.
You!
Your toes are like little sausages.
You!

Julie Prudence (8)
St Katherine's School, Snodland

A Teddy Bear

Curved ears,
Round eyes,
Fat stomach,
Glossy fur,
Furry face.

Sleeps nights,
Can't talk,
Loves sleeping,
Eats all day.

Eats everything,
Eats cakes,
Eats apples,
Eats pies.

Samantha Sibley 10)
St Katherine's School, Snodland

My Sleeping Cat

My secret with my cat,
He wears a pink hat.
He lays down on the mat,
He never plays with the rat.
Because he never wakes
He has lots of breaks.
He sleeps all day
And gets in the way.
He's very old
And his name is Gold.

April Baker (8)
St Katherine's School, Snodland

FOOTBALL CRAZY

I've got a brand new football, I play footie every day.
When I'm out on the fields, I really want to play.
I can't have it without my football it's too hard to miss
I play with it in the morning, in the evening, in the mist.
Though when I'm getting older, I just want to be
Like a David Beckham, Jaap Stam, or a goalkeeper!
I'd like to play at Old Trafford and standing near the goal
I'd put my strength into it, also my heart and soul.

Daniel Kelly (10)
St Katherine's School, Snodland

IN THE JUNGLE

In the jungle I can see a bear with a cup of tea,
In the jungle I can see a big bear with a key
And in the jungle I can see a snake feeding me.
In the jungle I can see a little bird singing to me,
And in the jungle I can see a big gun with a thumb,
And in the jungle I can see a little tum shouting for his mum
And all I can see is tea with a key.

Samantha King (8)
St Katherine's School, Snodland

IN THE LAND OF COO

In a jungle lives a tum,
Shouting for its mum.
Its mum won't hear him,
Because she's in the bin,
Looking for her tin.

Luke Rees (8)
St Katherine's School, Snodland

THE LAND OF THE FUNNY JUNGLE

In the land of the funny jungle
The tiger roared
And the monkey was bored.
The snake was wriggling,
The gorilla was giggling,
The koala was dancing,
The duck was prancing,
The cat sat on a log,
The worm slithered over the dog,
The gorilla is full of hairs,
The bear is eating twelve pears.
The witch is old,
The girl had lots of gold.
The day is hot,
The baby is rocking in her cot.
The rat is chasing Bungle,
In the land of the funny jungle.

Kirsty Streatfield (8)
St Katherine's School, Snodland

THE PIG AND THE WIG

A lady saw a pig,
wearing a wig.
It was spiky and wiggy,
and he was smoking a ciggie.
He was on rollerblades,
leaving people in a daze.
He was trying to get to the sales
to buy some scales.
He wants to get fit,
so he can play in the pit.

Amy Hall (10)
St Katherine's School, Snodland

IN THE LAND OF THE JUNGLE

In the land of the jungle
The tiger roared
And the bear snored.
He played his drum
And went home to fill his tum.
In the land of the jungle,
The monkey snored
And the dog was bored.
In the land of the jungle,
The duck went quack
And the cat was black.
In the land of the jungle
The tiger went 'Hoo'
And the mouse went 'Boo.'
In the land of the jungle,
The gorilla could climb,
He got there in time.
In the land of the jungle,
The tiger went 'Hoo'
And the mouse went 'Boo.'

Stacie Baxter (8)
St Katherine's School, Snodland

THE BAD BOYS

In the land of the bad boys,
They were making a noise.
They climbed a tree
And captured me,
And that's the end of me.

Obi Holloway (8)
St Katherine's School, Snodland

THE LAND OF THE FUMBLEY FLOO

In the land of the Fumbley Floo
There was a funny crew.
There was a monkey
That was so funky.

In the land of the Fumbley Floo
The monkey went down the floo
The monkey lost his hair
And he liked to eat a pear.
The cat went 'moo'
The dog went 'boo!'
In the land of the Fumbley Floo.

Keith Stickells (9)
St Katherine's School, Snodland

YOU!

You!
Your fingers are like walls.
You!
Your legs are like old, oily tools.
You!
Your nostrils are like mouse holes.
You!
Your arms are washing-up bowls.
You!
Your ears are like bird food.
You!

Ashley Lawry (8)
St Katherine's School, Snodland

THE CHANGING OF THE WIND

The wind is a cat,
playing, jumping up trees, catching leaves.
His purr covers the towns.
Dodging, pouncing through fields.
Which way? Left or right?
Leaping, diving, taking risks,
slowly he sits to rest,
then out he jumps, a full surprise!
Pushing, shoving anything he finds.
He comes, he goes,
slowly he tires and vanishes.

Out jumps the lion roaring like mad,
rocking the trees, leaping here to there.
People disappear into houses, leaving
him the whole town!
Weak trees have no hope,
he'll just knock them down.

Slowly night advances.
The cat slips through windows,
curtains ripple.

Emma Jones (11)
St Margaret's CE Primary School, Tonbridge

THE SCREAMING GALE

It's been an incredibly scary night.
The gate has been ripped from its hinges,
Lids blown off bins, litter everywhere.
Slates blown from the garage roof
And smashed on the ground,
The screech of the wind thrashing about,
Screaming.

Sometimes the gale sounded and acted
Like howling wolves.
A new full moon has been seen behind a cloud
Which swirled past,
As if boiling in a cauldron of wind.

Rosie Martin (10)
St Margaret's CE Primary School, Tonbridge

THE RAINMAKER'S CALL

Drought had cast its shadow across the wilderness
in which the Masai lived.
All the population was being slowly squeezed into death's door.
The land had lost its outer shell of beauty and
now looked pale and sickly.

It was time to get out the rainmaker again.
It was time to call the rain god to come and save them.

There it lay, slim and sleek, a thing of beauty,
this was the thing that was going to send their message,
the thing that would tell the god they needed rain.

Silence came. None moved a muscle as the chief
slowly moved the rainmaker up and down.

Then very slowly the sky let her tap drip.
Then it dripped faster and faster
until the tap was a bath draining water.

As more and more rain fell the paleness and sickliness
was washed away.
Rain had once again conquered the drought.

Sarah Reynolds (10)
St Margaret's CE Primary School, Tonbridge

My Raving Temper

My mother had a spectacular clock;
The most beautiful you could find.
People coveted it,
But to me, it was nothing.
If only . . .
If only the hands could turn back
It would not be shattered.
Mother was heartbroken.
Alone in my room
I should have thought for others' feelings,
Not just my own;
Distressed,
I wondered how my mother felt.
Could she ever forgive me?

Kaylie Vine (11)
St Margaret's CE Primary School, Tonbridge

Tribe

A tribe were sitting round a fire.
Where the moon shone in,
It made shadows
Over the mellow, yellow grass.
In patience the tribe waits.
Suddenly,
A powerful army of raindrops fell
Down from the sky.
The fire quenched,
It was pitch-black.
They danced, bumping
In to each other
With bliss.

Sophie Beard (10)
St Margaret's CE Primary School, Tonbridge

ANIMAL WIND

A breeze is a playful kitten
playing with butterflies,
jumping, running, catching.
The kitten turns angry and becomes a lion.
Roar! The lion runs across roads,
jumps fences and soon calms down into
a mischievous monkey.
Climbing trees and shaking branches,
the monkey gets bored and turns into a panther.
Camouflaged against the black sky
the panther plods along the road, then starts to run,
faster and faster,
until it is worn out and becomes a kitten again.

Tabitha Banbury (10)
St Margaret's CE Primary School, Tonbridge

WAITING

I wait outside
knowing they're discussing me.
I can feel it.
I'm frightened
about every thing.
What are they going to do?
Will they hurt me
or just leave me?
Worried, scared,
slouching on a bench.
When he emerges,
I know he will have bad news.

Sarah Bailey (10)
St Margaret's CE Primary School, Tonbridge

WIND

The wind is like a Tasmanian devil,
Uncontrollable and fast.
Hunting anyone out of doors
Greeting them with stinging eyes,
Like a scorpion's sting.
It runs round between trees
Shaking them and making
Leaves dance to the ground.
Howling down the streets like owls,
Then destroying and sweeping
Up anything in its path:
Taking lids off dustbins
As if looking for food,
Before emptying it over the gardens.
Then it slows down, dying,
Its breath grows longer,
It weakens and falls,
The wind dies down,
The wind becomes a cat,
A playful breeze,
Quietly moving away,
Brushing your cheeks.
A slight purring comes from faraway,
Tampering and splitting the clouds.
The sun comes,
Like a dog,
Frightens the wind away!

Thomas Gilbert (11)
St Margaret's CE Primary School, Tonbridge

THE FIRST RAINDROP

Dull colours
as I wait for the rain to come.
I sit with my rain maker
calling out,
I hear thunder from afar.
The clouds are dimming into darkness
as the noise gets closer.
I tip my rain maker slowly
and there I see the first drop.
I run out and dance around
in the rain.
As they fall and splatter on the
ground,
I see crimson, bronze, navy and greens
sparkle in my eyes.

Emily Bailey (9)
St Margaret's CE Primary School, Tonbridge

THE RAIN STICK POEM

I sit and see the wet season come,
The first falling droplets start,
They scatter and burst the ground.
Our thanks are to the rain stick.
They dance and sing around the growing waterhole.
I remain seated on the ground in my hut
As pitter-patter-pat falls on the straw roof.

Ashock Stally Chudasama (9)
St Margaret's CE Primary School, Tonbridge

UNDER THE DROUGHT'S CLAWS

The sun was setting across the savannah,
the colours luring the sun to bed.
The drought bleaching colour
from the Kenyan landscape.
A boy calling rain,
his tribe giving up.

Suddenly a big drop,
a wall of dust blinds the plains.
Rain has come!
People emerge from huts shouting for joy!
Trees soak up water,
grass turns from a dry, sanded colour
to lush green, dew like diamonds.

Season after season has past,
early morning
the drought has spread.
Father and son
looking out in despair.
He passes the rain stick
hoping it will work for his son,
like it did for him!

Sophie Guillum Scott (10)
St Margaret's CE Primary School, Tonbridge

MYSTERIOUS MIST

It soars over seas,
Bringing blindness to the ships.
Silence fills the air,
The waves seem to freeze.
Dipping and diving, the rocks
Blocking the view of the sun.
The owl has arrived with mist.

It swoops through the forests,
Over the mountains above.
It seems a blind has fallen
On to everything around.
The mist rises,
Revealing streams and rivers.
The owl has gone once again.

Holly Baldwin (10)
St Margaret's CE Primary School, Tonbridge

LEAPING FROM ROOF TO ROOF

Leaping from roof to roof is a horse.
He gallops across the landscape,
his mane flying,
his feet light as a feather.
His whinny sweeps across the ground,
snatching all objects in its path.
Sometimes his hooves thunder
over the earth,
sometimes they make nought
but a whisper.
His body is as soft as a pillow,
but if he shoots past you,
your cheek stings like a wasp.
Sometimes he likes to vault
through trees,
and rattle the leaves as he hurtles
between the branches.
He tangles your hair mischievously,
laughing at your anger.
His name . . . wind.

Rebecca Field (10)
St Margaret's CE Primary School, Tonbridge

ST CLEMENTS

Father, please not to St Clements!
This carriage is pulling me closer to another term.
The torture, the cruel pain rushing through my heart,
Twelve girls, twelve iron beds, they laugh, they jeer.
My only friend is my Bible.
When they see me; the proper me,
They'll forget all the rumours, they are history now.
They will see I can run and race through my reading,
But until they see . . .
This carriage is pulling me closer and closer
To another term of torture at St Clements!

Becky Finch (11)
St Margaret's CE Primary School, Tonbridge

WAITING FOR THE RAIN

The African plains are windy
As the tribes wait with wonder
For the first thunder of rain.
As the sun lies down, all the
Colours disappear in a puff of smoke.
Still the tribe waits.
Suddenly a bang was heard,
Up the tribes jumped and started
Playing their rainmaker.
With joy, the tribes fall fast asleep.

Charlotte Bailey (9)
St Margaret's CE Primary School, Tonbridge

WIND

The wind is a butterfly
floating down the streets
flowing through the meadows
and fields, taking all its time.
It never needs a rest
for it will never die.
The wind is a butterfly
floating down the street.

The wind is a wolf
whining through the streets.
He is sleek and silent, fast and smart.
Wandering through the unknown lands
and the undergrowth, he stalks his prey
with care.
A wolf whining through the streets.

Dan Lyons (10)
St Margaret's CE Primary School, Tonbridge

LONELY

Travelling alone.
Countryside for miles.
Opposite me I see families together;
No one lonely.
Every minute I pray that life will be fine.
Three stations away lies the dreaded orphanage.
I regret the things I said to my mother . . .
It's too late.

Charles Jones (11)
St Margaret's CE Primary School, Tonbridge

BONNIE

She eats from her bowl,
She's as black as coal.
She likes playing with you
As all pups do.

Pouncing on flowers
For hours and hours.
Digging huge holes,
Like a sleek, shiny mole.

She nips and she growls,
She creeps and she prowls.
She's terribly funny
And her name is Bonnie!

Miles Foxley (9)
St Margaret's CE Primary School, Tonbridge

THE TASMANIAN DEVIL

The Tasmanian devil twisting and turning
Trying to blow umbrellas inside out
Causing destruction wherever he goes
Ripping houses apart
Throwing people around
Causing tidal waves
Flooding the village
The wind is the Tasmanian Devil.

Aaron Smith (9)
St Margaret's CE Primary School, Tonbridge

THE EVERLASTING SEARCH

The sky is a red mist,
staring down on the traveller,
watching as he seeks his prey.
Drought was his homes invasion,
his rain stick as his only hope,
water is his destiny,
he calls out in despair.
Gradually a rain bomb hits the ground,
explodes,
water falls from above,
explosives set off from all over the sky.
Celebration at home,
the earth is alive again.

Phoebe Courtley (9)
St Margaret's CE Primary School, Tonbridge

HIT OUT

I'm grumpy; moody, stressed.
Content I should be but I'm not.
I've got faith; they'll forgive.
Sitting, waiting, will it happen?
Reading to a teacher for detention
Bible I shall read.
It was a cloak but I wanted a coat.
The coat was lovely, beautiful and warm.
It was as red as a rose.
I should have known better.
I should have not hit out,
A tantrum never succeeds
And I've lost a friend.

Tommy Ashby (9)
St Margaret's CE Primary School, Tonbridge

A LITTLE GIRL

A little girl all alone,
without mother or father.
All she has to comfort her
is a Bible.
Frightened and cold,
she thinks her mother and father
will return.
She does not accept they are dead.
She waits longer and longer,
it gets darker and darker,
colder and colder.
She has to face the truth,
she slowly begins to rise,
takes her Bible and leaves.
She walks through the dark and
misty night.
She sees a tall, lean man against
a post.
Perhaps her father is not dead!
She runs towards him,
her heart beating fast.
She slowly turns,
it's not him.
She cries,
slowly walks away.

Carla Cooper (11)
St Margaret's CE Primary School, Tonbridge

THE WIND

The wind is a lion roaring over town.
The trees rattle in fright.
It hunts the leaves out of frightened trees.
It runs around the countryside leaving footprints in the air.
The lion munches the crunching leaves.
While smashing the roofs and chimneys.
He roars at the people, running through the towns.
He grabs the hats off of people and throws them all around.
He laughs while they jump up and down
to catch their hats.

Sian Chaney (10)
St Margaret's CE Primary School, Tonbridge

RAIN, RAIN COME AGAIN

One cloudy night
People were gathering
Noise, rain shaker, rattle, rattle
Waiting for rain
Getting impatient
The rain came
It was not what they expected.

Paul Baker (10)
St Margaret's CE Primary School, Tonbridge

THE WIND

A lion is a rainfall
It's a beast thundering down
Its nasty, scary, boisterous roar
rings throughout the forest.
It's brawny, it's brave
it thunders down like a plane.
It splashes through trees
and crashes down on leaves.
Slipping, sliding everywhere
rain crashes down like a lion.

Karl Storey (10)
St Margaret's CE Primary School, Tonbridge

THE FLIGHT OF AN EAGLE

The wind is an eagle soaring through the streets,
rattling the roof tiles and screeching, screeching,
fluttering the canopy and creaking the gutters.
Swaying the trees and bending the flowers,
slashing at the window open, open.
Flattening the grass, finding a place to rest,
finally settling down on the top of a tree and
sleeping, sleeping, sleeping, sleeping.

Nik Van Mol (9)
St Margaret's CE Primary School, Tonbridge

THE ENCHANTED BOX

A silver face of a well remembered friend,
this box made of clay sits on a shelf,
in memory of my first ever dog, Diamond.
I know it's only a model,
but it seems there is a whole new world
when I lift her head,
to reveal what's inside, this enchanted box.

Maybe she's there, maybe she lives a
second life inside this box.
I can hear her when the world is silent,
just a slight noise a rustle.
I am sure she is there.

You can hear her paws thudding on the ground,
but I still can't understand how she is there,
or if it's only a slight sound.
Deep in my dreams.

Clare-Marie Dobing (11)
St Margaret's CE Primary School, Tonbridge

THE WIND IS A WOLF

The wind is a wolf
howling through the tree dancing
with the leaves
Sun turns to moon
The wind summed his strength
When autumn turns winter he dies and he's again
The gentle breeze comes again.

Harry Webb (9)
St Margaret's CE Primary School, Tonbridge

THE LONELY CHILD

The room was empty,
her feelings cold,
the bench hard.
She sat bolt upright,
stiffened with fear.
The nursery was quiet,
she felt a sudden gush of wind
from the open window,
but she sat waiting.
The door creaked, she didn't move.
She was like a wax doll,
stiff with smooth skin,
her clothes finely ironed and
scented with an aura of light and warmth
but she sat waiting,
waiting and thinking,
thinking about the governess,
knowing she was coming.
Wanting to get it over and done with.
A knock at the door. Was it her?
But still she sat waiting.

Andrew Simmons (11)
St Margaret's CE Primary School, Tonbridge

PLAYING FOOTBALL

Up, up and away goes the football,
up in the sky like an apple pie but
trying to come down with the player in
the air, I thought I could see him
but I don't know where.

Where is he? I'm not sure but
I think he's there, right on the floor.
But up he goes again in the air
with the player kicking
him fast as a hare.
The ball comes down into the net,
the goalie dives and gets all wet.

Joshua Pickup (10)
St Ronan's School, Hawkhurst

THE FLYING ORANGE

The Flying Orange was hanging on the tree
but then suddenly it went up, up and away
and went through the leaves
of the big tree and looked like and orange football
A boy caught the Orange
and Orange was scared
The boy thought it looked tasty

But the Orange went so high
in the air
that you could not see it
and the Orange said 'Ha, ha you can't get me'
The Orange was amazed and it flew away
from the boring Old Kent Road and flew
over the lorries, cars and people
The Orange landed in America and saw

An orange tree and then he was chased
by a man with a net
But the Orange was too fast and landed on a tree
and settled down with some new friends.

Alex Macintyre (9)
St Ronan's School, Hawkhurst

THE CUPBOARD UNDER THE STAIRS

They're there, I can feel it under the stairs,
Gathering together, silently, in pairs,
Waiting to creep up at night,
To eat all our food, and hiss and bite.

I crept down the stairs with a chill down my spine,
I opened the door and there was an eye,
Cold and green, and with a spark,
It stood up and hissed in the dark.

I screamed and ran up the stairs,
Mum and Dad ran down, hopping like frightened hares,
They calmed me down and put me in bed,
I pulled the covers over my head.

I got up and crept down the staircase,
Slow down, I thought it's not a race,
My heart beating fast I swung open the doors,
'Don't hurt me,' I said, it extended its claws.

It was dark and I squinted my baffled eyes,
It lay there quietly and it began to rise,
I raised a trembling hand to it,
'Miaow,' it said, I named it Kit.

Hugo Kemball (10)
St Ronan's School, Hawkhurst

THE PLANE JOURNEY

Up in the air, across the sky
Whiz! Whiz! Whiz! Fly! Fly! Fly!
Round and round the propeller goes
We're nearly there the pilot knows
We fly across cars and fields and trees
And lots of bushes with all their leaves
We're nearly at the airport now
There's a cat on a roof top
Miaow! Miaow! Miaow!
As we land there is a jerk and a bump
And when we stop, out we jump

When we get home we shout
'Hip hip hooray'
And when I go to bed
'Goodnight,' is all I can say.

Niall MacCrann (10)
St Ronan's School, Hawkhurst

THE DRAGON

T   he dragon takes off
H   e runs along the ground
E   ventually he lifts up off the ground

D   aringly he flips over in the air
R   ony the other dragon comes
A   fter that he feels sick
G   roosse! he has just been sick
O   n Rony's new jumper
N   ow Rony's absolutely mad.

Anna Munro-Faure (10)
St Ronan's School, Hawkhurst

THE SPITFIRE

The Spitfires are taking off
He goes up, up and away with
Exhaust fumes behind the Spitfire
'Stop the shooting, we'll waste our ammo,' said the pilot

Pip was the pilot
I was the gunner
The other Spitfires were next to me
'Fire at will,' said the pilot, 'enemy ahead'
I fired rapidly , my best friend died
Reinforcements had arrived and we won the battle
'Eureka, we've won,' shouted Pip
And we both got medals of honour.

Charles Beecroft (10)
St Ronan's School, Hawkhurst

UP, UP AND AWAY

Up goes the bullet faster than I can see,
lodged in the bird's guts.
    I say ha ha ha hee hee hee.
    There lies the bird as dead as can be.
    I know that my Mum and Dad would suspect me.
So I chucked it in my friend's garden on their compost
heap to burn next week.
    Branches and branches, twigs and leaves piled up
on top of each other, to make a big heap and on
that a poor dead bird.

Marc Faure (9)
St Ronan's School, Hawkhurst

JUMPING BANANAS

Bananas look boring
And not very tasty,
But when they are jumping,
You start going crazy,
They ruined the dumpling,
The one for the party,
The neighbours were saying,
What is all that thumping.

You could not sleep,
With the bananas
And at the day of the party,
The bananas were still here,
But the party stayed on,
But after five minutes,
The guests had all gone
And now I know,
Bananas aren't boring.

Charlie Houghton (10)
St Ronan's School, Hawkhurst

THE FLYING CARROTS

Moles and rabbits living under the ground
Roots of carrots hanging down
Beavers running along the ground
Rabbits jump up in shock
And carrots come out of the ground
Up, up and away they go and
Come back with a bump.

Edward Page (9)
St Ronan's School, Hawkhurst

THE WINGED PANCAKE

The pancake was hot and ready to eat
I flipped it too high
Into the sky
It grew some wings
And soared through the sky
It grew a mouth
And shouted 'I'm free, I'm free
You will never catch me'
I picked up a net
I started the chase
But it was obvious
He would win the race
I cried 'Come back, come back'
But I was far too slack
He shouted 'Go eat a hen'
But I wanted a pancake
So the chase went on
But not for too long
I gave up in the end
The pancake went back to his family
In the baker's
Only to be turned into a cake
Which I had to make
So I had some breakfast in the end
With ever growing sorrow
For my pancake friend.

Hugo Brodie (9)
St Ronan's School, Hawkhurst

WAR!

B ullets fly
U p, up and away
L odge themselves into the enemy
L ogs and trees as well
E ntirely by mistake
T he bullets fly

B ang, bang!
A nd another bang!
N one too many
G oing at a time

B lood and guts go flying
A nd people as well
'N ot again please,' says everyone
G o to hell!

Charles Weston Smith (11)
St Ronan's School, Hawkhurst

UP, UP AND AWAY

The plane goes high,
Right up in the sky,
You better not be scared of heights
Otherwise you might get the frights,
Look at the sea,
There's a shark,
It might bite,
Its teeth look very white,
We might land soon,
Landing is such fun,
I'm glad we're nearly done.

Edward Grissell (8)
St Ronan's School, Hawkhurst

THE FLYING PANCAKE

My mum made a pancake.
She flipped it
and it went
up
and up
and came down.
'Don't touch it!'
she said to my
brother, who
at once took
it and
flipped it.
It went up
and up
and it didn't come down.
It went on
and up
and on
and up
and it still didn't come down.
It hit the ceiling
and it still didn't come down.
It stayed there.
My mum came and looked at it
but it still didn't come down.
My dad came and poked it with a
stick, but it still didn't come down.
When we had tea
my brother looked at it and it came
down
and down
and it stopped on my brother's face.

Kiloran Campbell (9)
St Ronan's School, Hawkhurst

THE CATAPULT

Out of the catapult goes the stone
up, up, up the stone goes
The stones goes up higher than I can see
over the fence to my neighbours garden
going rapidly towards the house
falling in height going towards the window
I ran behind the tree saying ha ha ha hee hee hee
knowing that they would know it was me
It hits the window shattering it entirely
shards of glass falling down onto their lawn
A head pops out of the window cursing me
I ducked low, as I could see the head scanning the area
Then went back in
I ran across the garden as fast as I could
and ran to my room.

Bertie Blundell (9)
St Ronan's School, Hawkhurst

JETS

One happy day I went to the airport
And then a driver asked me
'Would you like to drive a jet?'
'Yes, please,' I shouted
Then he took my hand
And he showed me around
And I said 'Please let me
Drive on my own'
'Okay'
I shouted 'Cool!'
And it was fun!

Alex Kelin (10)
St Ronan's School, Hawkhurst

UP, UP AND AWAY

T   hose witches, they fly so high above the sky,
H   olding their cats, just above their laps,
E   xcept for Ethel whose cat sits on the back of her broomstick,

W   itches, they fly so high above the sky,
I   f I were a witch I wouldn't itch my stockings,
T   he witches at the academy all have cloaks,
C   hildren all have cats at the academy,
H   ow do they do it? No one knows,
E   xcept the witches themselves,
S   o make sure you don't get turned into a frog or your mother
     might not be too happy.

Michelle Faure (8)
St Ronan's School, Hawkhurst

UP, UP AND AWAY

Up, up and away high
We can fly above the sky
Above the clouds - makes me sick
And if you're scared of heights
You're in for a fright
There's nothing to see in that misty sky
Except the clouds
It's really dull and boring
An the journey makes my ears ache
And gives you a headache
It's fun and fast when you land
And sometimes when you take off.

Harry Hoblyn (8)
St Ronan's School, Hawkhurst

BASEBALL

B aseball in my opinion is a brilliant game.
A ball is bowled towards you and you whack it with a club.
S imple it may seem but whatever you do, do not swing
E ast. The ball flies, the crowd goes wild and
B last! The ball has been caught and you're out.
A t that moment the crowd boo and hiss, the game has stopped.
L eft, right, the batter walks up and down the pitch, then suddenly
   he gets into his place, the
L imit, the crowd gets noisy, he hits it and America win the match!

Jonathan Ross (8)
St Ronan's School, Hawkhurst

AEROPLANE

A plane takes off
E arly in the morning
R ight through the clouds it goes
O ver the mountains
P eople looking out of the windows
L aughing at people skiing below
A fter an hour or two everyone was asleep
N ight had come over the mountains
E arly in the morning the plane lands - it has arrived.

Toby Walker (9)
St Ronan's School, Hawkhurst

FOOTBALL

F   ootballs flying through the air
O   ver the goal post some land there
O   nto the players skilful foot
T   owards the goal
B   ut the goalie saves this ball
A   nd another shot is taken
L   anding smashing into the back of the net
L   ots of people cheer and wave.

Marcus Hall (10)
St Ronan's School, Hawkhurst

BASEBALL

B   alls, balls floating around
A   nd some still on the ground
S   trike 3 and you're out!
E   veryone groans without doubt
B   ecause their best players are gone
A   t New York everyone has a banner
L   oads and loads and loads of fans
L   ike the New York Yankees.

Edward Beecroft (9)
St Ronan's School, Hawkhurst

UP, UP AND AWAY

Kite
flies high
above the ground
leaving me
behind.

Balloon
big, hot
air balloon
whooshes up
frightening
animals on its way!

Flying squirrel
a scruffy
silly squirrel
flies
like a rocket
whizzing through the air.

Charlotte Peniston (8)
St Ronan's School, Hawkhurst

BALLOON

B   rightly coloured and large
A   irwards and upwards
L   ifting off and sailing along
L   eaving behind a trail
O   f dust along the road
O   ff the land it goes
N   ever to be seen again.

Alastair Borland (9)
St Ronan's School, Hawkhurst

UP, UP AND AWAY

Umbrellas go up, up and away
Planes go high in the clouds
Unicorns fly like a bird in the sky
NASA rockets fly to the moon
Dogs leap as high as your knees
Ants climb the tree to the top
Water splashed high in the air
Acrobats flip high in the air
Yachts glide high above the bottom of the sea.

Charles Harris (8)
St Ronan's School, Hawkhurst

TRAVEL

T   ravel sometimes makes people sick, or maybe even happy
R   ight through the air or under the ground, maybe by train
A   nd these days you can go just about anywhere
V   ia a road so you don't have to pay
E   very time you go somewhere
L   anes or dual carriageways you can go a long way!

Ben Wilkinson (10)
St Ronan's School, Hawkhurst

UP, UP AND AWAY

Up, up and away this amazing bird just flew away.
The eagle has a beak sharper than a needle.
It saw a flamingo prettier than a stained glass window
Then it caught its prey!
For the eagle it was a wonderful day because it caught its prey.
Up, up and away this amazing bird, just flew away.

Theo Kingshott (8)
St Ronan's School, Hawkhurst

YOU AND I

You are everybody's greatest friend,
I am not so popular.

You will score loads of runs,
I blow it by getting you run out.

You answer maths problems really quickly,
My brain goes all fuzzy.

You can run really fast around the field,
I can barely run around my back garden!

You can be really sarcastic,
I just stare in awe.

You have won the spelling contest,
I can just about spell cat!

You keep on going until you've succeeded,
I give up after five minutes!

You stay on your surfboard for hours on end,
I might as well just swim.

You can play many musical instruments,
I am only mediocre at the symbols!

Even though you are everybody's friend,
I think you like me the most!

Ciara Masterson (11)
St Teresa's Catholic Primary School, Ashford

YOU AND I

You are good at eating;
I won't eat cabbage
You concentrate when you work;
I won't write a word
You are the brains on the computer;
I can't hit a key
You can run for miles on end;
One step hurts my feet
You can hit a golf ball miles;
My golf ball goes two inches
You can sleep all day and night;
I won't shut my eyes
You make chocolate all creamy and sweet;
I make chocolate all gungy and melted
You choose all the latest clothes;
I go back ten years
     You are oh so better than me;
     But you are still my friend.

Jonathan William Fearne (11)
St Teresa's Catholic Primary School, Ashford

YOU AND I

You show off like there's no tomorrow,
While I'm normally too scared to talk.

You could easily eat the house down,
While I take a year to chew.

You could run off as fast as the wind,
While I have to shout, 'I'm right behind you.'

If you play the keyboard, proper notes come out,
I play it and all the windows smash.

You are better than me, at a lot of things,
But we are both as good, at being friends.

Alexander O'Malley (10)
St Teresa's Catholic Primary School, Ashford

YOU AND I

You can do tricks on the skateboard;
I can't even skate.
You are good at football;
I am good at netball.
You are excellent at art;
I swing the brush round and my picture's ruined.
I play on the computer and win;
You can't even get past the first level.
I keep my room in a mess;
You keep yours neat and particular.
I would bungee jump for a dare;
You wouldn't climb a tree.
You can dance while ice skating;
I take one foot off the ground and slip.
Your hair can be different in many ways;
I can only put mine in one style.
I jump a lot when there's a surprise;
You run around the house, screaming.

    The only thing that I can say is . . .
    You're the best.

Kandice Fernandes (10)
St Teresa's Catholic Primary School, Ashford

YOU AND I

You go to town and socialise,
I stay home and complete work.
You keep fit and look real cool,
I can't play sport, I am no good.
Your hair is long and wavy,
Mine is short and greasy.
Your dance moves don't have spare beats,
My dance moves have spare beats.
Your brother rides a motor bike,
Mine doesn't know how to drive.
Your clothes are hip, flash and cool,
Mine are old and unfashionable.
My brother gets on my last nerve,
Your brother makes me laugh till I cry.
Your parents know the latest trend,
Mine just drive me *crazy!*

Rachel Leavey (11)
St Teresa's Catholic Primary School, Ashford

YOU AND I

You can play the clarinet beautifully;
When I play the roof falls down.
You can fit into the lowest of places;
I am taller, so I'm found first.
You can fool people to get a cheap ticket;
I look older, I pay the full price.
I can play the flute like the bird;
When you blow, my ears ache.
I can fix my painting to look good;
If yours goes wrong, the world seems over.
I can get into the cinema easily;
You don't look old enough to see the film.

I can do tricks on my skateboard;
You only stand on it and pretend.
We're very different with our own talents;
But that just makes us closer friends.

Nicola Perry (10)
St Teresa's Catholic Primary School, Ashford

YOU AND I

You can get into clothes that are tiny
I can't get into anything small

You can get into all the photos
I just get pushed away

Your handwriting always gets a star
I just get bad remarks

You can work out all the sums
I can't minus one

You can eat hot chilli peppers
I can't eat a curry

You can do fancy ice skating
I have a record for falling over

You could swim a mile
I would sink halfway through

You always come first because you are the best
I have to face it, I am not good at anything
that you can do.

Grace Kettle (10)
St Teresa's Catholic Primary School, Ashford

YOU AND I

You jump like a frog,
I can't even hop.
You are a whiz kid,
I am slow like a snail.
You dash like the wind,
I trip like Mr Blobby.
You dance like a pop star,
I dance as if I am drunk.
You sing like an angel,
I sing like a wolf howling.
You write neat and tidily,
I scribble like a baby,
Even though we are not the
Same we are still friends.

Amanda Jowett (11)
St Teresa's Catholic Primary School, Ashford

YOU'RE BETTER THAN ME

You're as fast as a cheetah,
I'm as slow as a tortoise,
You can lift an elephant,
I can't lift a feather,
You're such a comedian,
I can't even tell a joke,
You're the greatest at football,
I can't even kick a ball,
You're like Di Vinci at art,
I can't draw a straight line.

Maggie O'Sullivan (10)
St Teresa's Catholic Primary School, Ashford

YOU AND I

You speak Spanish fluently;
I stumble over every word.

You run and whiz past;
I run, puffing trying to keep up.

You got a silver in disco;
I trip over my feet.

You are nearly grade one in tap;
I would never get that good.

You gracefully pirouette;
I spin and fall over, dizzy.

You eat large and tropical;
I eat small Chinese and Mexican.

You jump clean over the hurdle;
I jump, the bar wobbles.

You walk in great long strides;
I walk in toddling little steps.

You swim lengths upon lengths;
I get tired after one.

Hannah Quinn (10)
St Teresa's Catholic Primary School, Ashford

BETTER THAN YOU

I am fab at football,
Your pass goes an inch.
I just sit and listen,
You giggle like a hyena.
I can order a pizza,
You're scared to pick up the phone.
I wear some fashionable clothes,
Yours are ripped at the sleeves.
I can whack a sixer,
You're bowled and I appeal.
I can swim a mile,
You drown after a length.
I can write inch perfect,
You're not bothered but sloppy.
But even though we have differences,
You will always be my friend.

Matthew Burchett (11)
St Teresa's Catholic Primary School, Ashford

YOU AND I

You can jump higher than the wall and higher than me
I can't jump as high and I'm not as tall
You are good at football and at playing hockey
I can't head a ball, I get hit by the puck
You are good at mountain biking over the ramps
I can't even get over the first jump
You can play the recorder, more than I can play
I can play the recorder but only one damn note
You are the best at everything
I wish I was nearly the same as you.

Mathieu Walsh (11)
St Teresa's Catholic Primary School, Ashford

YOU AND I

I can swim the English Channel,
You can't swim five metres.

I sing with the voice of an angel,
You go out of tune and break glass.

I am described as a computer whiz,
You can't even work a mouse.

I crack problems in a jiffy,
You are still there several hours later.

I am trusted to do a job,
You can't even eat without causing a problem.

I draw like a cartoonist for Disney,
You draw like a five year old.

I have the guts to ride high rides,
You can't even go on the tea cups.

I would go sky diving if I could,
You would say that your afraid of heights.

I am calm and quiet,
You are loud and blary.

Although we are good friends and we play together,
All the time, we are good at different things.

Emma O'Brien (11)
St Teresa's Catholic Primary School, Ashford

YOU AND I

You get top marks in spelling tests
I get such a lousy thirteen
You go to town to socialise
I stay at home to do homework
You score hat tricks time after time
I get put back in defence
You run as fast as a ray of light
I couldn't even beat a snail!
My ball flies over into next door's garden
Yours goes right where you want
I walk to school on foot
You drive your flash limo

Although we're completely
Different
You're still my best friend.

Morgan Davies (10)
St Teresa's Catholic Primary School, Ashford

YOU AND I

You could run for miles on end;
I run only in slow motion.

Your tap is elegant and fine;
My tap is not that great.

You eat small and petite;
I eat large and monstrous.

You jump and leap energetically;
I hate to do anything hot and bothering.

You speak so calm and carefully;
I stutter to speak when I read out aloud.

Your ankle turns all stiff and stern;
My ankle turns all slow and slack.

You are a fine cartoonist;
I couldn't draw a face on a person.

Maddison Leigh Coke (11)
St Teresa's Catholic Primary School, Ashford

YOU AND I

You're the best at football,
I can't kick a ball.

You're a slogger batsman,
I get bowled first ball.

You can swim The Channel,
I drown straight away.

You write really neatly,
I can't hold a pen.

You create great art,
I just rip the paper.

You're really great at tennis,
I just hit the net.

I know I may sound useless,
But I still know you're better than me.

Elliot Hulland-Kemp (10)
St Teresa's Catholic Primary School, Ashford

FLATTERY WILL GET YOU NOWHERE

You can belt a football
I just tap it an inch
You can do 50 lengths
I just sink to the bottom
You can draw great art
I just doodle a face
You can be fab on PlayStation
I can't work out the moves
You can write really neat
I just spill the ink
You have a pool in your garden
I prefer the bath
You can times big numbers
I can only add them
You have charisma to burn
I am out of the crowd
Flattery will get you nowhere
But you're definitely better than me.

Michael Sparks (11)
St Teresa's Catholic Primary School, Ashford

BETTER THAN YOU

I am the best at swimming,
You can't even do 25 metres.

I am the best at hockey,
You can't even hit the ball.

I am the best at maths,
You can't even add up 10 and 10.

I am the best at sports,
You just can't be bothered.

I am the best at horse riding,
You're scared about falling off the horse.

Danielle Sarah Ratcliffe (11)
St Teresa's Catholic Primary School, Ashford

I LIKE, YOU LIKE

I'm the best at line dancing,
You can't do the steps.
I like to hold snakes,
You shiver when one's around.
I like to play netball,
You'd rather play football.
I like playing guitar,
You're never in tune.
I enjoy drawing,
You just think it's boring.
I enjoy modern dancing,
You prefer singing.
I'm faster at running,
You get puffed out when walking.
I like to hold cats,
You jump when it goes miaow . . .
I always giggle,
You have a quiet laugh.
I might be good at something,
But you are good at other things.

Jessica O'Reilly (11)
St Teresa's Catholic Primary School, Ashford

YOU AND I

You can climb to the top of trees,
I only manage halfway.
You can do excellent tricks on your skateboard
I end up with a series of grazes.
You run like a cheetah,
I walk like a tortoise.
You do sums in your head,
I have my trusty friend's paper and calculator.
You run with the ball at football,
I get tackled and hurt.
You remember lines in drama,
I go red and bite my lip.
But there is one thing I'm better than you at,
I have finished this poem,
You have only just started.

James Aglony (10)
St Teresa's Catholic Primary School, Ashford

YOU AND I

You can remember everything;
I have to write them down.

You can dodge everyone at football;
I get tackled at midfield.

You can jump like a kangaroo;
I can just reach the 2.5m mark.

You can sprint a mile;
I get a stitch.

You master football skills;
I just sit and watch.

You climb a dozen trees;
I climb two.

You can help me to improve;
I help you to improve.

Alex O'Connor (11)
St Teresa's Catholic Primary School, Ashford

YOU AND I

You are faster than a car
I am like a snail
You're like a rubber, you're so flexible
I'm like a pencil, as stiff as wood
Your concentration is really good
I'm in a world of my own
You get high marks in maths
I can't even get half marks
Your work is so neat
I can't even get it half normal
You're good at football
I can't even kick a ball
You act like a human being
I am like a person from the planet Zog
You can get your homework in on time
I can't even get mine in
You can draw really well
I can't even draw an apple
You are the best at acrobatics
I can't even do a forward roll.

Rachael Bailey (11)
St Teresa's Catholic Primary School, Ashford

YOU AND I POEM

I love to swim
You hate to go so deep

I'm fast at dancing
You can't keep your pace

I write neatly
You just scribble

I saw wood roughly
You just tear it smoothly

I'm the best at the hula
You can't make it spin

I'm speedy on bikes
You can't stay on

I can paint
You just daub

I can play the clarinet
You just squeak

I can sing
You just yell.

Sarah Byrne (11)
St Teresa's Catholic Primary School, Ashford

SPRING

Spring is here
Again this year,
Flowers are blooming,
Skies are clear.
The birds all sing
Their happy song,
Reminding me
That winter's gone.
I open my window,
Look down the lane
And see the trees
All green again.
Spring cleaning time
Has come around,
Long lost oddments
Now are found.

Freja Ludlow (8)
Shernold School

SNOOPY

Snoopy's on the trail
Looking for a snail
Going down a valley
He went up a hill
Where there was
A windmill
Blown away
By such a windy day.

Sophie Sandison (9)
Shernold School

I WANT TO BE . . .

I want to be a pop star
When I grow up
To win something like an Oscar
Or to win a cup.

I want to be a teacher
And teach in Shernold school
I'll be quite a good teacher
I won't be a fool.

I want to be a P C
To help people understand the law
I won't be able to stop for tea
We'll help stop crimes even more.

I'd love to be an air hostess
To fly through the air
I want to be one of the best
But really I don't care!

Mira Ambasna (10)
Shernold School

MY DOG

I have a dog called Dodger,
He is brown and white,
He jumps up on my bed, every day and night,
He always gives me company,
Every minute of the day,
I will never want to sell him,
No way!

I love my dog so much,
He loves me too,
He is a pest sometimes,
But I don't mind at all,
No way!

Sarah Crouch (8)
Shernold School

HOMEWORK

Homework, oh homework,
I hate you, you stink,
I wish I could wash you
Away down the sink!

Uh oh, here comes Mum,
I'm in trouble now!
'Have you done it yet?
What have you been doing for the last hour?'

Where shall I start?
There's so much to do,
Maths, English, French,
I know, I'll stick my picture on with glue.

That was easy!
Now time for real work,
My head is spinning,
I'm going berserk.

'Mum I've got a headache,
I want to go to bed'
'Well you can't until you've got
Those tables in your head!'

Abby Savage (8)
Shernold School

MY ACTING CAREER

I want to be an actress
For all the fame and fortune it brings,
I'm sure it will be loads of fun
And I will meet many stars.

Julia Roberts is my idol,
For she is very cool
And stars along side many actors,
For instance, Richard Gere.

She seems to enjoy herself
And earns plenty of money too,
So that's the reason why
I want to be an actress
And one day I will!

Emma Ghosh (8)
Shernold School

MY NEW DAD

My new dad is cool
He's funny and smart
He makes my mum happy
He makes me laugh
He listens to me
He gives me advice
He helps me at netball
He is very, very nice
He cheers me up when I am sad
I'm really pleased he's my new dad.

Alessandra Scala (8)
Shernold School

A DONKEY'S DREAM

I wish I were a unicorn,
Not a donkey on the sand.
I'd have a shining, magic horn
And not a leather band.

I wish I were a racing horse
And not a plodding mule.
I'd be the first on every course,
Instead of playing the fool.

I wish I were a giant shire
And not a donkey born.
I'd never be a horse for hire,
My saddle old and worn.

If wishes were horses,
Then I'd be one soon.
If horses had wishes,
We'd ride to the moon.

Rosemin Anderson (10)
Shernold School

HAIR!

I'm great without hair.
Hair! Hair! I hate hair!
'No playing with your hair!' said the teacher.
Nobody cares I have no hair.
Hair on my head.
My mum says,
'The nits don't stand a chance.'

Ellie Bliss Chirnside (9)
Shernold School

PUPPIES

Puppies are soft and very sweet
When they are good they deserve a treat
Puppies are fun
Puppies are fine
I wish I had one that was all mine
We would go for long walks some of the time
and play in the garden in the sunshine
I would come home from school
and give him his dinner
and then run some races to see who's the winner
Then we come in and have a long rest
I would hug my puppy because he is the best.

Alexandra Allin (8)
Shernold School

FIREWORKS

Fireworks go whizzing round,
Fireworks are very loud.
Watch Catherine wheels go round and round,
You better watch them before they hit the ground.
Watch the rockets go banging off,
Watch them banging in the sky.
But don't get one in your eye.

Fireworks are very pretty,
But I think they're loud.
Everyone loves fireworks except *me!*

Laura Howell (7)
Shernold School

THE METAL COW

I wish I had a metal cow
I'd milk it with a spanner
And every time the milk came out
I'd hit him with a hammer!

But all I have it a golden goose
Whose head is always coming loose
Yesterday it fell upon the floor
And now I can't find it anymore!

So now I'm begging on knees
Please, please, please, please
If anyone sees a metal cow
I really need one right now
I really need one right now!

Jade Jasmine Francis (10)
Shernold School

THE FUTURE

The future might have flying cars,
People might have landed on Mars,
There might be aliens from out of space,
With a body smaller than its face,
People would discover unknown creatures,
Also with unknown features,
People will stop pollution,
That's my best solution,
The future is a place of new inventions,
Now let's go forward in anticipation.

Charlotte Lepora (9)
Shernold School

WHEN I GROW UP

When I grow up I want to be
a keeper in a zoo
To look after all the animals
and keep them healthy too
I'd love to watch the elephants
have their daily bath
spraying water everywhere and
making people laugh
Then there are the chimpanzees
who love to mess about
just like naughty children
they play and fight and shout
I'd love to do as they do
go swinging in the trees
climb up ropes and leap about
but not to scratch for fleas
and all those funny penguins
like waiters in a queue wearing little
dinner jackets and wobbling fro and to
The reptile house is creepy
with lots of beasts to meet
Beware of slimy lizards and things
with shiny teeth
This is the way when I grow up
that I would like to be
but as for now the stables and my horse
will do just fine for me.

Natalie Brockwell (10)
Shernold School

SLEEPING DOGS

Dogs asleep,
ah . . . how sweet!
All in a ball
until you call
the magic word 'Walkies!'

Do dogs ever
dream?
If so, do they dream
of chasing cats by the
ream?

As they dream,
they curl up in a
ball.
You can't tell if they're
big or small, or even if
they're there at all!

Jane Costello (10)
Shernold School

MY FAMILY

My mum is nice and very kind.
My dad is OK and not too bad.
My brother is a monster but very cute.
My aunt is good at sewing.
My nanny is very kind and playful.
My grandpa is useless and falls asleep.
My grandma lets me come round to stay.
My grandad reads me stories.
That's my family.

Amy Hartfield (7)
Shernold School

SCHOOL

The ugly bell starts the day,
'Clear the path and make way.'
Children screaming
Children dreaming
of the day ahead.

At ten-past nine the day begins,
Soon there'll be overflowing bins.
But still you know you have a good school,
Maybe with a swimming pool!

But one day you'll remember it,
Maybe just bit by bit!
These memories you'll love them so,
School, school, school!

Rachel Crane (11)
Shernold School

THE SEASIDE

The sea crashes against the sand,
And the sand becomes the sea.
The sea goes back out,
And leaves behind shells and pebbles in the sand.
The shells twinkle in the sunshine,
All sparkling and clean.
The pebbles are hard and sharp in the soft sand.
The sea is blue and very big,
With lots of different fish, crabs and lobsters,
And sharks live there too.

Victoria Webb (7)
Shernold School

SLEEPING DOGS

Fast asleep, stretching out.
Dreaming of dreams, that might come true.
Waking up, feeling hungry.
Spots a rabbit,
Forgets his hunger.
Hoping and wishing he will catch it.
Waiting and waiting for it to come closer.
He hears a voice.
Could it be true?
It is shouting 'Dinner, dinner!'
Forgets the rabbit.
Makes a run, for what he thinks will be a treat.
But he's wrong, it is just chicken.
Tries to find the rabbit, but sadly it's gone.
He goes back to sleep.
Stretched out by the fire.
Hoping his dreams might come true.

Alice Bettney (11)
Shernold School

SUNSHINE

The sun is very old,
It shines yellow and gold.
It shines bright in the sky,
Like a lantern hung up high.
The sunshine is nice to play in,
It's like a big, gold sequin.

Rebecca Harris (8)
Shernold School

MY NEW HAMSTER

My new hamster is called Lilly.
She is just so, so cute!
She is seven weeks old.
I bought her on Sunday, 30th January.
I gave her the name Lilly and she likes it a lot.
We put her in her wheel and she
runs around the house.
She walks around her tubes and eats a lot of food.
She looks really sweet and cute when she sleeps.
She runs and walks all over you,
that means she
loves
you!

Victoria Edwardes (8)
Shernold School

THE ISLE OF WIGHT

When I went to the Isle of Wight,
it was sunny, I went to the beach.
When I went back to the flat,
we went swimming.
It was dark when we came back,
I had to go to bed.
The next day we had to take the
dog for a walk on the beach.
Then we went on a boat to catch some fish.
They smell like the beach.

Jennifer Cosgrove (7)
Shernold School

My Saturday

On Saturdays I get up at seven,
Then watch TV till half-eleven.
Then I have my Coco Pops,
And go down to the shops.
I always buy my weekly mag,
As well as ten sweets in a bag.
By then it is time for lunch,
And for ten minutes I sit and crunch.
Next it's time to walk the dogs,
We always run around the same old log.
Then I throw the ball for Max,
And when I get home I sit and relax.
At that time it's half-past three,
And then again I watch TV.
After that it's time for tea,
I always have spaghetti.
Then I read for half-an-hour,
And sleep to charge up my power.

Francesca Lepora (11)
Shernold School

Speaking Computers

Speaking computers are magic
And everyone else is tragic
And if you're quick on the keys
You will be very pleased
To have the use of a computer
When the computer speaks
　　　　　it makes a beep.

Cara Heffernan (8)
Shernold School

ROLLER DANCING

Skating is a lot of fun
Until you trip and fall on your bum.
Go through the merits,
Whiz past the graders,
Now I'm learning
the right way.
A 'sit spin' makes you
very dizzy,
a 'flying camel'
makes you very
whizzy.
Our teacher Nina is always busy.

Natalie Hayon (8)
Shernold School

MY CAT

I have a cat,
Who's very fat,
He spends his whole day
Sleeping his life away
The only time he ever wakes
Is when he gets a stomach ache
With this huge hunger pain
He finds it quite a strain
To leave his cosy house
In search of a mouse.

Jemma McCulloch (10)
Shernold School

SLEEPING DOGS

Curled up in a ball,
sound asleep,
dreaming.

Rolled up pups on
owners' laps, dozing.

Sound asleep
on beds, sofas,
and under hedges.

Head on pillow,
body on bed,
lying next to you
having a nap.

Sound asleep,
no chance of
waking.

Eyes closed,
not a care
in the world.

Dreaming of catching
cats, darting across
the lawn.

Charlotte Pryce (10)
Shernold School

DESPAIR

She was lonely
She was sad,
She walked the streets
She wasn't bad.

What had she done
To come to this?
No roof tonight
So much to miss.

The cardboard box
So grim and cold,
No running water
No sheets to fold.

To Benefit Office
The daily rush,
For endless hours
The queues that push.

She walks the streets
So short of food,
Her head hangs low
In blackest mood.

Charlotte Reid (11)
Shernold School

SLEEPING DOGS

Old dogs
spend most of
their day asleep,

Curled up
in a ball
just like a hedgehog,

Snoring loudly
dreaming of chasing rabbits
twitching whiskers on the go,

Twisting, turning
In the sunlight,

Waiting, waiting
just waiting
for the aroma
of spaghetti bolognese,

Rolls off his bed
jumps up
and has another dinner
as well as tea to drink.

Katrina Colebourne (11)
Shernold School

JESSICA

My little rabbit Jessica nibbles
away on her gnawing log every day.
She hops up and down and over the ladder.
She twitches her nose and wriggles her feet.
She sleeps on her hay every day
And then she wakes up, hop, hop, hop.
Her favourite food is her harvest munch bar
which she has as a treat once a week.
I love her to bits and she will always
be my little rabbit, Jessie.

Alice Clarke (7)
Shernold School

HOW I TURNED INTO ME

I wonder how I came to be me?
I think I squished and squashed.
Now I know my mum became fat
I was unsteady like a newborn calf.

I didn't like Heinz for dinner,
So I went for slugs.
I didn't go fast,
I didn't go slow.
I went quite fast.
I also went slow.

I got older and older,
Bigger and bigger,
Faster and faster,
Cleverer and cleverer,
And now I am me!

David Gillet (7)
Slade Primary School

THE HOODED COBRA

A smooth-slitherer
An aggressive-hisser
A secretive-predator
A skin-shedder
A sneaky-burrower
A sly-coiler
A hood-displayer
A poisonous-killer
A tongue-revealer
A nasty-biter
A mouse-stalker
A food-swallower
A scaly-monster
A grass-flattener
A vole-devourer
A man-frightener.

Jake Mountain (11)
Slade Primary School

THE TREE

A maggot shape,
A worm shape,
A caterpillar shape,
A bird-flying shape,
A frog shape,
As rough as sandpaper,
As green as seaweed,
I felt small,
I like that tree because I do.

Jessica Winchester (7)
Slade Primary School

ANIMALS AROUND THE WORLD

Animals around the world are different,
depending on where you go,
go to Africa to the zoo,
in Australia you may meet a kangaroo,
this kangaroo may have eyes, a nose and a mouth,
because they live only in the south.
In the jungle you may find a tiger,
it may have stripy claws and a stripy back.
In some parts of the world you will find a lion!
This lion may have a golden mane and a big face.
One more animal I like is a cheetah
with a spotty body but,
                    it may eat you!

Joseph Makey (9)
Slade Primary School

DAD'S PATIO

My dad built a patio,
He did not know where the slabs should go
Bigger and bigger it grew and grew
Slab by slab until he was through.
Pop the corks, light the lights,
Play the music, party all night.
Games to play, food to eat

            My dad's patio,
                    oh what a treat!

Samantha Downs (8)
Slade Primary School

CHARLTON

Charlton, Charlton you are the best,
Charlton, Charlton you are going to beat the rest.
Charlton, Charlton we are going all the way,
Charlton, Charlton I love to see you play.

Charlton, Charlton, Hunt scores all your goals,
Charlton, Charlton let's see the ball in the net.
Charlton, Charlton all the tickets sold,
Charlton, Charlton will never forget.

Charlton, Charlton we are going to win the cup,
Charlton, Charlton we are going to go up.
Charlton, Charlton we will beat Man City,
Charlton, Charlton all the way to Wembley.

Michael Mason (8)
Slade Primary School

SILVER

As silver as a hanging crystal chandelier
As silver as a falling tear.

As silver as frosty trees
As silver as the Seven Seas.

As silver as a bubbling lagoon,
As silver as the gleaming moon.

As silver as a waterfall, cascading from a cliff,
As silver as a supersonic spinning disc.

As silver as a sparkling marble rock
As silver as a ticking clock.

Michael Mumford (9)
Slade Primary School

TOUCH! WHAT CAN YOU FEEL?

Touch!
What can you feel?
The shiny scales of a glittering fish
swimming skilfully
through the sea.

Touch!
What can you feel?
The spiky sharp quills of a
porcupine, but,
keep away, never stay
or you'll get a spiky surprise.

Touch!
What can you feel?
The hot, blowy haze from an extractor
fan, misty, hazy, hot.
The cold hard moments of an icicle.

Touch!
What can you feel?
The fizzy, whizzy contents of Coke.

Joe William Venables (8)
Slade Primary School

MY SPECIAL FRIEND

I like to take my dog for a walk
She's funny, I wish she could talk.
She's not very big, she's quite small
She runs down the garden to the end
I wish she could live forever
My special friend.

Mark Underdown (7)
Slade Primary School

250

SNAKES

Snakes long, snakes short,
Snakes fat or even thin,
Sharp fang, no fang,
Land snakes, sea snakes.
Black mambas, green mambas,
Snakes black, snakes green,
King cobras, spitting cobras,
Flying snakes, frilly snakes.
Squeezers, slitherers,
Shedding snakes, dashing snakes,
Boa snakes, boomslang snakes.
Snapping snakes, strangling snakes,
Dull snakes, colourful snakes,
Forked tongues, pointy tongues,
Smooth snakes, egg-eating snakes,
Adder snakes, horned snakes.

Lewis Daniel Partington (8)
Slade Primary School

ONE TWO THREE

One oval orange
Two twin sisters
Three TVs with turtles on them
Four F1 cars racing by
Five fancy cars firing smoke
Six silly girls singing a song
Seven silly boys singing a stupid song
Eight monsters eating eight pieces of cake
Nine naughty boys making stupid noises
Ten toys jumping off a bed.

Lewis Richardson (8)
Slade Primary School

THE HAUNTED HOUSE

The haunted house is spooky,
the haunted house is dark,
it's creepy and it's scary.

There are spider webs in there!

All the windows are broken,
the floorboards too.
My mum wanted to move there
but I refused to, *so there!*
I got my own way,
I should have gone with Mum
I had to live with my best friend.
I had to use her toothbrush
I had to use her hairbrush
Well, I'm better off now so
I don't really mind.

I dare you to go in the
                    haunted house!

Emily Avis (9)
Slade Primary School

FRIENDS

Friends are very fun people,
Rich or poor,
It doesn't matter,
Everyone needs a friend,
No one should have no friends,
Don't worry if you don't . . .
            You have one now!

Catherine Harris (8)
Slade Primary School

BEDTIME

Oh I hate my bedtime
I moan every time and say 'No!'
When my mum finally got me up to
the bathroom
I do everything really slow!

One hour later Mum shouts
'Are you ready yet?'
Footsteps come up the stairs
What shall I do?
What shall I do?

I had already done my teeth
so two more things to do
Mum is halfway on the stairs
I quickly wash my face
She's on the landing so
I quickly put my pyjamas on
and when she opened the door
I was there already.

I refused to come out and my
mum was really cross, she dragged
me to my bed and said goodnight
and that's what happens every night.

Geoffrey Wagstaff (8)
Slade Primary School

IF YOU WANT TO SEE A TIGER

If you want to
see a tiger you
must go down
into the dark
dark and deep jungle.

I know a tiger who
lives down there you
don't want to meet,
he's furious, he's a growler
he's waiting for his tea.

Yes, if you want
to meet a tiger you
must go down into
the dark, dark and deep
jungle.

Go down into
the dark jungle
and say
'Tiger dada
tiger dada
tiger dadaaaaaaaa!'

And out comes
the fearful tiger
jumping around
but don't stand
there because he'll come
and really bite you.

He'll really rip
you to pieces
and he'll grab
at you and so
run for your life!

Emma Smith (9)
Slade Primary School

THE GORGEOUS MAN

His attitude is as sweet as candy
He's as playful as Milly Molly Mandy.

He is funny
And as cute as a bunny.

I love the gorgeous man.

When he runs past
My heart beats fast.

He is gorgeous
And was born before August

I love the gorgeous man.

He is built like a stick
And is as strong as a brick.
When I look in his eye
I think of the blue sky

I love the gorgeous man.

I will smile when we walk down the aisle
If we ever do!

Charlotte Simpson (9)
Slade Primary School

THE MONSTER UNDER THE BED

Who is it under the bed?
Who is it flapping the sheets?

'Who is it?' I said to my mother
'Who is it?' I said.

Who is it drumming their fingers?
It's the monster under the bed.

Who is it hissing down there?
What is the murmur I hear?

'What is it?' I said to my mother
'What is it?' I said.

What is it groaning my ears out?
It's the monster under the bed.

Why do I have to hear it?
Why do I have to know?

'Why is it me?' I said to my mother
'Why is it me?' I said.

Why is it him down there?
The monster under the bed.

How did it get there?
I thought in my head.

I looked and I screamed
I saw it come close

A big black nose
A pale white head
The monster under the bed.

There I was
My mum came in

'There you are Whiskers!
Under the bed!'

Rachel Balcombe (9)
Slade Primary School

PEACH, PEAR, PLUM

In the garden I picked a peach
It was hard to reach
Alex picked a big pear
She stood on a chair
Thomas picked a red plum
Helped by a little chum

We made a small round pie
We looked at the sky
Alex wanted one more pear
Tom had taken the chair
Thomas looked with big eyes
And shooed away the flies.

What a lovely day in the sun
We have had lots of fun
Mum had a long rest
We picked the very best
The end of the day
We must go away.

Hannah Moore (9)
Slade Primary School

WHO IS THE MOST POWERFUL LADY OF ALL?

Mirror, mirror, on the wall,
Who is the most powerful lady of all?
Will I marry a slave
Of the prince who lived in the castle?
Will I marry a rich man,
With more than twelve million pounds?
So answer me - please,
Who is the most powerful lady of all?

Mirror, mirror, on the wall,
Who is the greatest flyer of all?
Is it the whitest dove, or me?
No - it can't be her,
She's always having babies.
Is it Peter Pan, or is it me?
No - it can't be him,
He watches too much TV
So answer me - please
Who is the greatest flyer of all?

Tanya Portch (7)
Slade Primary School

MATHS

Maths, who likes maths?
Adding, subtracting, take-away
All of those numbers just get in your way.
Long division, decimal points
If you're good, you'll get a team point
1 + 1 = 2, 2 + 2 = 4.
Miss, how much more?

Emma Jennings (8)
Slade Primary School

HALF ANT, HALF HUMAN

If I were an ant
I'd be rather thin
I won't like that
at all.

But if I were
human I'd be OK
I haven't a clue
what to be.

But if I were
half ant, half human
I can be both

If I were
half ant, half man
'Why don't you shut up'
my mum says. 'Now
be quiet and up to bed.'

Paige Elizabeth Capeling (8)
Slade Primary School

A SCHOOL OF STARS

My grandma is very kind
She helps to swim, she doesn't mind
The ladies in the playground are
                    fun to have around
I work hard and need a rest
My teacher gives me a star,
I think she's the best.

Rowan Nicholls (8)
Slade Primary School

My Dad Joe

My dad Joe gets half his food from Farmer Groe
He makes remarks like this
'Oh you twit' and 'Oh my God!'
And my mum says
'Don't say that, that'll teach our son rude words.'

My dad gets mad then he forgets who he is
He starts attacking, 'He's mad,' I shout.
I phone the police, they arrest my dad
For ten years, that's why I only
See my dad once a year.
I only see him an hour every year,
OK, he's mad but sometimes he's OK, I don't care
He's my dad with fair hair.

Jack Maynard (7)
Slade Primary School

My Annoying Sister

My sister, she's really annoying
but I don't know why
She scribbled on my drawing.
My sister is really annoying
because every time I shout at her
she punches me and it really hurts.
My sister is really annoying
she thinks she's the best at everything
but she cries all the time, that's annoying.
Now you know my sister is annoying.

Evelyn Salter (7)
Slade Primary School

TINY FAIRY

At the bottom of
the garden where
the river flows there
was a little fairy
whose name was Bows.
The next day she was
still there but building
a little home. After night
I could not believe my eyes
Bows had sent invites to
all her little friends.
I wonder if Bows will
ever go away? I will never
know until the next day.

Rachel Annetts (8)
Slade Primary School

ONE, TWO, THREE

One orange octopus eating an orange.
Two tigers teaching teacher.
Three teachers teaching tigers.
Four flowers flicking flies.
Five flying flies.
Six sizzling sausages.
Seven slipping tigers.
Eight elephants flying.
Nine knick-knacks.
Ten tigers running.
Eleven elephants running.
Twelve new tigers.
Thirteen brand tigers.

Kim Straeche (8)
Slade Primary School

THE TIGER

The tiger lives in the jungle,
His coat is orange like the sunset
With black stripes,
He has long sharp teeth to bite,
Claws that scratch other animals.

The tiger is really, really big,
He has a long tail,
He runs fast,
Chasing animals to eat.

The tiger sleeps in the bushes,
When he wakes up he makes a loud growl,
He wakes up every animal,
The tiger is hungry and he looks for food,
Today he will eat another animal.

Georgina Wickham (7)
Slade Primary School

SPACE

No oxygen to breathe,
No gravity to hold us down
Only an endless universe of stars, planets, asteroids, and
Galaxies like a giant food chain.

Some say there is life in space
Intelligent life from Mars!
Space is a massive undiscovered world.

Thomas Vorley (8)
Slade Primary School

How I Feel

I feel angry when people say nasty things to me

I wish I had my hearing aid back.
I wish my nose was fixed because it's silly.
I really hate people saying nasty things.
It does my head in.

I feel dizzy because I've had lots of operations
But it feels horrible.
I wish my implant was in.

When I feel happy I'm at home playing on my computer,
Game Boy Colour.
I wish I had Game Boy Painter.
I wish I had a PC.

James Colvin (8)
Slade Primary School

Flowers

Flowers smell lovely, beautiful, sweet.
They grow in the rain and in the heart.
With colours of red, orange, blue,
Yellow, white and purple too.

They start from a seed and grow so tall,
There's even some that creep up a wall,
Some are painted and some are round,
On hills and gardens can be found.

They're chewed by rabbits and liked by bees,
When I walk through them they tickle my knees,
In the winter they close up tight,
But in spring, summer, they're a beautiful sight.

Amy Coats (8)
Slade Primary School

IF YOU WANT TO MAKE A DRAGON

If you want to make a dragon
Remember to give him crushing jaws with crushing teeth,
With a massive tummy underneath!

If you want to make a dragon,
Remember to give him a long green tail,
And speed so he can run a million times faster than the average snail.

If you want to make a dragon,
Remember to give him dark poisonous smoke,
Which will make everyone cough and choke.

If you want to make a dragon,
Remember to give him massive gleaming eyes,
Which will make you scream out millions of times!

If you want to make a dragon,
Make sure no one is near!

Dominic Madar (8)
Slade Primary School

ONE, TWO, THREE

One orange octopus eating an oak tree.
Two twin turtles talking to a telegraph pole.
Three tigers that weigh one whole ton.
Four fat fiddlers fiddling along the riverbank.
Five fat frogs farting loudly.
Six slithery snakes sliding after some slimy slugs.
Seven slugs being attacked by people sprinkling salt.
Eight earwigs nipping explorers' bottoms.
Nine additional dictionaries doing numeracy.
Ten tiny tinkerbells tapping on the trees.

Charlie Gregory (8)
Slade Primary School

A RAINBOW

As red as a hose,
As red as a rose,
As red as a nose,
That someone blows.

As orange as a stain.
As orange as a frame.
As orange as a flame.
Flickering in a lane.

As yellow as a bun,
As yellow as the sun,
As yellow as a gun,
Glinting in the sun.

As green as the sea,
As green as a tree,
As green as a pea,
I had for tea.

As blue as a sign,
As blue as a pine,
As blue as a line,
I drew so fine.

As indigo as a mesh,
As indigo as a vest,
As indigo as a dress,
Worn by a pest.

As violet as a map,
As violet as a hat,
As violet as a mat,
Slept on by a cat.

Rachel Boyce (9)
Slade Primary School

MY FAMILY

Mum's the best
She makes our breakfast
And washes all my clothes
Especially my brother's socks
Which make me hold my nose.

Dad's great
He mends the gate
And mends the car as well
If he gets too tired
He has forty winks
In his comfy chair.

Shaun's my brother
He's like no other
Sometimes he gets on my nerves
At the end of the day
He lets me play
Racing on his PlayStation.

Laura Griffin (8)
Slade Primary School

THERE WAS A FOX

There was a fox
who lived in a box.
He wore red socks
and his friend was an óx.
He went to the shops
to buy Coco Pops.
And stole seven tops
but got caught by the cops.

Hannah Lowe (8)
Slade Primary School

BABIES

Babies are a treat
And very sweet.
Babies can't talk
But sometimes walk.
Babies can be smelly
And have a small belly.
It's hard to sleep
If you chew your feet.
Babies love their mummies
And suck on their dummies.
It's double the trouble
If you have two!
If you smile at them
They will smile at you.
I have two brothers
One is Ollie
He is a wally!
My other brother is called Jake
When he gets big he might get a toothache.

Sam Brinton (9)
Slade Primary School

MY NAME

D   is for Dan, that is my name.
A   is for animals that I used to have.
N   is for noise that my drums make.
I   have a CD player that is brilliant.
E   is for every Friday I do swimming and boys' brigade.
L   is for laughing that I do quite often.

Daniel James Potter (8)
Slade Primary School

MY DAD

My dad is so funny
He's bald and he's fat.
He lives up the road
And he's got a big cat.

He goes out to work
And he drives a car.
My sister and I say
He's the best dad by far.

He snores by night
And shouts all day.
He's got a big mouth
My sister says.

In the summer we go
Down to Gran's.
Wherever we walk
He makes me hold hands.

At Christmastime
It's brilliant, it's fine.
But whenever he drinks
He spills all the wine.

On my birthday
He took me to the Dome.
When we went to the 'rest' part
And he laid on his own.

When we went to see
Toy Story 2,
I sat on my chair
And he trod on my shoe.

So that's the end
About my dad.
I love him to bits
And he's a really good lad.

Jessica Francis (9)
Slade Primary School

EXPIRED

I am a fox in a white winterland,
Hungry and cold as I usually am,
As I approach a dark country farm,
I think of tender chicken safe in their barn,
I wouldn't dare, the farmer might be around,
I look carefully without making a sound,
I spy the bin,
And think what might be within,
As I flick off the lid it makes a great crash,
To me the contents are precious food, to the farmer it's trash,
Suddenly I hear the sound of a gun,
Every sense in my body screams run, run, run!
But I can't, as I feel a stabbing pain,
Not a soul hears as I yelp out in vain,
As I hit the ground,
My heart starts to pound,
Nobody cares about me or my fate,
All because of some scraps which had gone out of date.

Jessie Purchase (10)
Slade Primary School

THE NOCTURNAL VISITOR

He comes at the dead of night,
When the sky is dark and the stars are bright.
Silently, creeping along, a flash of red,
When I'm warm and cosy tucked in my bed,
He scavenges for food from garden to garden,
Rummaging through bins asking nobody's pardon,
He sniffs the air expecting danger,
His pointed ears pricked, expecting a stranger,
A bushy tailed creature, the fox is my friend
To the fox my love I send.

Olivia Disandolo (10)
Slade Primary School

IT'S BORING

I'm bored when I go to the hairdressers
because I'm always last.
I'm bored when I go to Sainsbury's
because I don't get what I want.
I'm bored when I go to school
because we don't do maths all the time.
I'm bored when I go on holiday
because I have to sit still for so long.
I'm bored when I go to my nan's
because there's nothing to do.
I'm happy when I play on my N64.

Matthew Luff (7)
Slade Primary School

ON A FROSTY MORNING

Glistening dew shining brightly,
like sequins on a wedding dress.
Melting snow clinging strongly on branches,
like syrup sticking to a spoon.
Thick footprints indented softly in the frost,
like the bump left by a hammer.

Thin, bare trees shivering wildly in the breeze,
like clockwork teeth out of control.
Little robins tweeting sweetly around us,
like whistles blowing all at once.
Shiny stars disappearing quickly into the dawn,
like fireworks flying into the sky.

Long empty hedgerows flapping in the wind
like paper in front of a fan.
Rabbit warrens clogged with hard snow,
like a crack filled with cement.
Tall hills overlooking the land,
like a CCTV camera is watching you.

The spring sun pops up,
like a flower opening.
All these give the birth of life to spring,
like a chick being born.

Andrew Storey (10)
West Malling CE Primary School

ON A FROSTY MORNING

When I see the frost outside,
Children love to run and slide.
Bare trees stand still and dead,
I wish the world was warmer instead.

Outside there's frost all glimmery,
On trees there's leaves all shimmery.
The grass is wet and cold,
The wind can bite you I am told.

Old cars all icy and white,
Dogs outside bark with fright.
A roaring wind comes down the street,
I watch, outside from my cosy seat.

Little footsteps trail along,
The steps of a bird singing a song.
People walk by on this frosty day,
The sun comes up and melts it away.

Robert Richardson (10)
West Malling CE Primary School

ON A FROSTY MORNING

Morning comes, the crisp frost sets.
Glitter rushing across the lake,
Like ripples in a swimming pool.
Gleaming cobwebs sparkle wildly,
Like stiff nail polish.
Dawn approaches, the sun comes up
Without a sound.

Danielle Cheney (9)
West Malling CE Primary School

On A Frosty Morning

Misty skies moving slowly
like feathers falling off a bird
on a windy day
crispy frost wildly setting
on the dark roof tops
in the morning.

Frosty grass sparkling lightly
like a horse just been washed
iced cars gleaming wildly
like newborn babies
bare trees standing coldly
like a frozen lake flowing stiffly.

Danielle Davis
West Malling CE Primary School

On A Frosty Morning

Shining grass blowing quickly
Like waves in the sea.
Clear sky shining brightly
Like a star in the galaxy.
Scared pets worrying wildly
Like people running rapidly away.
Windy trees flapping scarily
Like bikes going extraordinarily quickly.
Stiff cars standing still
Like glue drying swiftly on models.
Colourful frost glittering softly
Like a little puppy getting stroked.

Aaron Nixon (9)
West Malling CE Primary School

THE FROSTY MORNING

Lots of frost melting quickly,
Like a lolly left in the sun.
Big houses standing stiffly,
Like quick cement just put down.

White ice sparkling brightly,
Like tickly stars in the sky at night.
Blue cars driving wildly,
Like animals in the zoo going mad.

Bright sun shining strongly
Like a muscle man in the funny circus.

Nathan Boyce (10)
West Malling CE Primary School

ON A FROSTY MORNING!

Crispy grass frosting coldly,
as I yank back the curtains,
cold branches snapping slowly,
while I'm playing in the snow.

Glittering footprints melting wildly,
like clouds fading in the sky,
icy roofs sparkling brightly,
like stars just cleaned,
frozen ponds trembling smoothly,
like a pupil being hit with a cane.

Kirsty Poile (9)
West Malling CE Primary School

ON A FROSTY MORNING

Crispy grass glistening beautifully,
like a fountain shower in the park.
Icy footprints melting coldly,
like clear echoey sounds on a bare floor.

Vicious path battling roughly,
like two brothers tumbling together.
Cold wind roaring ferociously,
like lions in agony at the circus.

Bright moon shimmering softly,
like a polished school hall on the first day back.
Shiny stars floating peacefully,
like a relaxed sunbather on a hot beach.

Adèle de Gray (10)
West Malling CE Primary School

ON A FROSTY MORNING

Sparkly cobwebs swinging gently
Like a tooth fairy flying side to side.
Stiff scarecrows torn apart
Like a tornado ripping and sucking things up.
White trees blown about
Like a big bowl of ice-cream being swirled around.
Icy puddles cracking rapidly
Like a stream of chicks swimming along.

Gemma Beadle (10)
West Malling CE Primary School

ON A FROSTY MORNING

Frozen leaves shining beautifully
like priceless diamonds in a jeweller's.
Stiff trees standing lonely
like marine soldiers in the army.

Frosty grass sparkling wildly
like a silver necklace.
Sweet birds singing softly
like trumpets in a band.

John Bennet (10)
West Malling CE Primary School

ON A FROSTY MORNING

Colourful birds humming beautifully like
trees swaying in the wind.

Frosty bushes glistening gently like
leaves crunching in the breeze.

Icy puddles crackling neatly
on a horrible frosty morning.

Lewis Sweet (9)
West Malling CE Primary School

Happiness Is . . .

Happiness is a super feeling,
when your heart reaches the ceiling.
At some point everybody feels this joy,
men, women, girls and boys.

Happiness is a joy that you can feel,
while running, jumping or eating a meal.
It is a super and lovely touch,
you can never get too much.

Happiness is a feeling that is so much fun,
if one feels happy it catches up with everyone.
You can be happy in many places,
you want to see the look on happy faces.

Charlotte Bailey (11)
Willesborough Junior School

The Moon On A Cloudy Night

The moon is like a fingerprint
blotted onto a dark blue background.
The moon is like a drop of paint
flicked by a giant's paintbrush.
The moon is like an angel
floating in the spare space.
The moon is like a dirty lamp
waiting to be cleaned.

Claire Cartwright (11)
Willesborough Junior School

SUMMER DAZE

I love the hot sun
on a summer's afternoon
or when it's night-time
the lovely white moon

On a summer's afternoon
I go down to the beach
and when I am down there
suntan lotion I need to reach

I think you will agree with me
that the summer is great
because I think the summer
is just like a mate!

James Downing (10)
Willesborough Junior School

THE EAGLE

He watches you with his evil eyes,
as he glides through the air.
With his wings spread out,
ready to catch his prey.
His beak is sharp and pointed,
his claws are crooked and strong.
He spots a helpless baby bird,
and dives down, down, down,
like a body falling off a cliff.
The mother comes back,
ready for the attack.
So he swoops back up into the air.

Megan Dundas (10)
Willesborough Junior School

THE MILLENNIUM DOME

It's fun, it's great, it's fab and big
It's a massive Dome
Friday night the clock struck 12
Everyone kept shouting
'Happy New Year' they said

Everyone set off fireworks, party poppers too
Bang and crack
Is all you could hear
You couldn't hear yourself think

Stop poverty, let's have peace
It's the start of a brand new year
Let's think of the poor
And how we can help them.

It's a new millennium!

Aimee Picton (10)
Willesborough Junior School